To Beryl Anne:

ALL LOVE FLOWS TO THE SELF

Who is glowing in the bliss of the Self herself —

with much love

Ali xx

ALL LOVE FLOWS TO THE SELF

Eternal Stories from the Upanishads

KUMUDA REDDY, M.D.
THOMAS EGENES, PH.D.
LINDA EGENES, M.A.

SAMHITA PRODUCTIONS
Schenectady, New York

The Sanskrit quotations from the Upanishads at the end of most stories
are from translations by Maharishi Mahesh Yogi.

ISBN 1-929297-05-X
Printed in Singapore

SAMHITA PRODUCTIONS
1537 Union Street
Schenectady, New York 12309
1-888-603-9171

We are deeply grateful to

His Holiness Maharishi Mahesh Yogi,

who has brought to light the full meaning

of the Upanishads and the practical

technologies of consciousness to

enliven this knowledge in everyone,

so that all may rise to enjoy perfection

in life—Heaven on Earth.

CONTENTS

ACKNOWLEDGMENTS

We would like to thank Drs. Susie and Michael Dillbeck and Roxie J. Teague for their invaluable insights and additions. We would also like to thank the photographers, Mark Paul Petrick and Michael Peter Cain, for their striking and beautiful images; Peter DeCicco for sharing his Indian minature painting by Rammu; Shepley Hansen for the cover and book design; Peter Freund and Eric Vautier for developing the Devanāgarī and transliteration fonts; Susan Shatkin for editing; and Martha Bright and Claudia Petrick for copyediting. Finally, we feel blessed with the support and love of our families throughout this project and throughout our lives.

INTRODUCTION

The Upanishads are a precious aspect of the Vedic Literature of India, the land of the Veda. It is the good fortune of the world at this time that Maharishi Mahesh Yogi has gathered the scattered, thousands-of-years-old Vedic Literature into a complete science of consciousness for its full theoretical and practical value.

Maharishi has brought to light the most profound understanding of Veda and the Vedic Literature—that they are the fundamental structures of Natural Law at the basis of the universe. Veda and the Vedic Literature are the unseen impulses of intelligence at the basis of the orderly evolution of the ever-expanding universe—which includes the orderly evolution of individual life.

With this understanding, we appreciate that the full meaning of the Upanishads is not found in books. Rather, the Upanishads are structures of our own intelligence, our own consciousness, our own Self—*Ātmā*—and can be directly experienced in the simplest state of our own awareness, pure consciousness. While reading stories from the Upanishads, it is important to remember that they are about the qualities of pure consciousness. Even though the stories describe the comings and goings of people and events, at a more subtle level of understanding, these stories describe the dynamics of consciousness found within everyone.

The connection between the Vedic Literature—the fundamental structures of Natural Law—and our own consciousness and physiology can be clearly seen in the recent discovery of Professor Tony Nader, M.D., Ph.D. Under Maharishi's guidance, Dr. Nader has found a precise correspondence between each of the different aspects of Veda and the Vedic Literature and the fundamental structures and functions of human physiology. This discovery shows that every one of us is Veda; everyone has the total intelligence of Natural Law and its infinite organizing power within their own mind and body.

The beautiful, evolutionary qualities of consciousness expressed by the Upanishads and all other aspects of the Vedic Literature—qualities such as unifying, harmonizing, enlightening, transcending, and blossoming of totality—are enlivened in the individual through the practical technologies of consciousness of Maharishi Vedic Science℠, the Maharishi Transcendental Meditation℠ and TM-Sidhi® programs, including Yogic Flying. The result of practicing these technologies is that our thinking and behavior become more creative, life-supporting, and free from mistakes—more in harmony with Natural Law, and therefore more and more successful and fulfilling.

This is the daily experience of millions of people throughout the world who practice the Transcendental Meditation® and TM-Sidhi programs—that health, happiness, mental potential, and harmonious relationships grow naturally and spontaneously. Over 600 scientific research studies conducted at more than 200 universities and research institutions in 30 countries have confirmed the benefits of the Transcendental Meditation and TM-Sidhi programs for all aspects of life—mind, body, behavior, and society. Those who practice these technologies will find that, as they read and re-read these stories from the Upanishads, deeper meaning unfolds, reflecting deeper experience of their own intelligence, their own Self.

The Upanishads especially focus on the ultimate reality of life; they express the full glory of the Self, by gaining which nothing else is left to be gained. The Upanishads bring out that at the highest level of human development, the true nature of the Self, Ātmā, is wholeness, the totality of Natural Law, *Brahman*. From this level of experience, everyone and everything is as near and dear to us as our own Self; one flows in universal love, nourishing everyone and everything.

Traditionally, the Upanishads were passed down from

teacher to student. *Upa-ni-shad* literally means "to sit down near." Maharishi explains this as "everything sits down near the Veda." In other words, when we know the essence of everything to be Veda, then we have gained the fruit of all knowledge.

The Upanishads contain beautiful and exhilarating phrases such as "Thou art That" (*Tat tvam asi*), "I am Totality" (*Ahaṃ brahmāsmi*), and "All this is Brahman—Totality" (*Sarvaṃ khalv idaṃ brahma*). These phrases are nothing less than descriptions of the supreme awakening of consciousness to its own true nature. They are known as "great sayings" (*mahāvākya*) because they describe the essential teaching of the Upanishads in compact expressions. Maharishi describes these sayings as the final strokes of knowledge from the teacher, which fully enlighten the student who is ready to receive them; then wholeness dawns in the awareness. In reading the stories from the Upanishads we are thus reminded of the flow of our life towards its supreme goal.

Maharishi explains that the Upanishads, like all other aspects of Veda and the Vedic Literature, were cognized by the great enlightened Vedic *Ṛishis*, or seers; the profound truths dawned spontaneously in the silent depths of their own pure consciousness. Their cognitions are expressed in the language of Nature, Sanskrit. According to the Muktikā Upanishad, there are 108 Upanishads, with ten principal Upanishads (*Īsha, Kena, Katha, Prashna, Muṇdaka, Māṇdūkya, Taittirīya, Aitareya, Chhāndogya,* and *Bṛihadāraṇyaka*). In this book, the name of the Upanishad is written under each story's title. Sanskrit words and phrases that appear in each story are listed in the Glossary at the end of the book, along with their pronunciation and meaning.

अयमात्मा ब्रह्म

Ayam Ātmā Brahma

This Self is Brahman.

Māṇḍūkya Upanishad, 2

SATYAKĀMA—THE SEEKER OF TRUTH

From the Chhāndogya Upanishad

Long ago, in a small hut in the dense forests of India, lived a boy and his mother. The boy's mother named him Satyakāma, which means "seeker of truth."

More than anything, Satyakāma wanted to live the life of a student, meditating and studying about Brahman (wholeness) in the dwelling of his teacher. To become a student, he had to know his father's family name, because in those times teachers only accepted students from certain families.

So Satyakāma went to his mother, Jabālā, and said, "Mother, I want to live the life of a student of sacred knowledge." Jabālā was pleased with her son's desire to study Brahman.

"Dear Mother, of what family am I?" Satyakāma asked.

"My name is Jabālā and your name is Satyakāma, and I do not know your family name, my precious son," his mother said.

"Then what shall I tell my teacher, dear Mother?" asked Satyakāma earnestly.

Jabālā led a pure life and knew the power of truth. "Tell him just what I have told you, my beloved son," she said.

With his mother's blessings, Satyakāma left his boyhood home. He walked through thick forests where the light of the sun never touched the ground. He saw foaming streams splashing on rocks. He passed by lakes as still and glassy as ice.

Soon he came to the home of the great teacher Gautama, who lived in his *āshram*, his Vedic school, by the edge of the forest.

Satyakāma bowed to the teacher in respect. "Please, honored Sir," he asked, "will you accept me as your disciple? With your blessings, I wish to become a knower of Brahman."

Gautama thought the boy looked healthy and bright. But to accept him as a student, Gautama had to know the boy's family background. And so he kindly asked, "Of what family are you, my boy?"

"My mother said to tell you that her name is Jabālā and my name is Satyakāma—and I know nothing more about my family," Satyakāma explained without fear. "So I am Satyakāma Jābāla."

Gautama was pleased that the boy's mother had taught her son to tell the truth. "Only one from the best of families could give this explanation so sincerely," he said. "I will gladly accept you as my student. Bring the firewood inside, my boy."

Satyakāma's heart felt warm with happiness. At last he would be able to study the knowledge of Brahman.

The next day, Gautama said, "I will now begin teaching you the knowledge of Brahman, which is called supreme knowledge (*Brahma Vidyā*). The first step is to know your Self." And so Gautama initiated Satyakāma in meditation to settle his mind and heart. With a quiet mind, Satyakāma experienced his own inner Self, which was like a vast ocean of silence.

After teaching Satyakāma to meditate, Gautama did something unexpected. He took Satyakāma to the pasture where hundreds of cows were grazing. To Satyakāma's surprise, Gautama separated out four hundred thin, weak cows.

"Take these cows to another part of the forest and live, my dear boy," he said. "Tend them carefully. You may return when they have multiplied to a thousand!"

Without any doubts in his heart, the obedient Satyakāma drove his four hundred cows to a lush meadow on the other side of the forest.

At first Satyakāma felt lonely, since he was all by himself in the forest. But he sang to the cows and they mooed back to him as he slept. Satyakāma began to enjoy his life in the forest. His cows ate nourishing green grass and drank pure water from a spring-fed pond. Satyakāma watched his cows grow plump and happy.

Satyakāma stayed many years with the cows, living a peaceful life in the warm grassy meadows and cool forest. His days began and ended with meditation. As his mind became more and more quiet, he was able to comprehend the profound wisdom his teacher had given him.

He carefully tended the cows, always finding rich pastures for their grazing. As Satyakāma grew older, the herd of cows began to multiply. However, he was so contented with his life of meditation and knowledge that he noticed neither the passage of time nor the increasing size of his herd.

Nevertheless, a profound change was taking place in Satyakāma. In his peaceful life in the forest, he was coming to know the Self. His mind became serene, his heart filled with love, and his face glowed with light.

Satyakāma never felt alone. He became friends with the proud peacocks, the rippling streams, and the swaying trees. He even became friends with the sun and the moon. Every living creature became part of his family. He remembered the saying his mother had taught him, "The world is my family" (*Vasudhaiva kutumbakam*).

At night, as the cows slept, Satyakāma gazed at the infinite span of stars, scattered across the sky like a thousand sugar crystals. He felt as if all nature were speaking to him. In the bright morning, the dew bathed his feet. White gardenias called to him with their sweet scents. Wispy clouds and distant rainbows delighted his imagination. Cool rain splashed his skin.

"All this beauty is a part of Brahman," he thought. "Everything that grows and decays is a part of the great totality." He felt that he, too, was a part of the eternal cycle of life.

One day, the head of the cows, a wise bull, spoke to him. "Satyakāma!"

"Yes, honored sir," answered Satyakāma, who respected all living things.

"We are now one thousand cows," said the bull. "Please take us to your teacher's hermitage. And I will teach you the nature of Brahman, which has many aspects."

"Yes, please tell me," said Satyakāma.

"Brahman shines from the east and the west," the bull told him, "and from the north and the south. This is because Brahman is everywhere. It is universal. This is one quarter of Brahman."

Then the bull said, "The fire, Agni, will teach you more about Brahman."

Satyakāma began to drive the cows back to his teacher's āshram. When evening came, he put a rope around a large area to protect the cows. Then Satyakāma lit a fire. He sat down on the west side of the fire, facing east. He gazed at the dark sky, filled with his friends, the stars. After some time, the fire, Agni, spoke to him about the nature of Brahman.

"Brahman is the earth and the atmosphere," said Agni. "It is the sky and the ocean. This is because Brahman is endless. It is without beginning or end. This is one quarter of Brahman."

Then Agni added, "A swan will tell you more about Brahman."

The next evening, after traveling with his cows, Satyakāma again lit a fire by the side of a river. He sat down, facing east, and saw a great white swan gliding down the river towards him. The swan began to teach Satyakāma about the nature of Brahman.

"Brahman is fire," the swan explained, "and Brahman is the sun. Brahman is the moon, and Brahman is lightning. This quarter of Brahman is light. Brahman is the light of life."

"A bird will tell you more about Brahman," the swan said.

The next evening, after settling his cows in a safe place beside a hill, Satyakāma again lit a fire. He sat down on dry soft grass, facing east. This time a purple sunbird bird flew down from the limb of a tree. Like silk woven with gold, its wings caught the brightness of the fire.

The sunbird sang, "Brahman is the breath, and Brahman is the eye. Brahman is the ear and also the mind. This quarter of Brahman is the seat, the resting place. Just as the eye is the seat of what is seen, and the mind is the seat of what is thought, so Brahman is the seat of everything. Everything rests upon Brahman."

Finally Satyakāma arrived at his teacher's dwelling. His teacher noticed how Satyakāma's face was shining, and he said to him, "I see that you have found Brahman. For it is said that the knower of Brahman has settled senses, a smiling face, freedom from worry, and has found the purpose of life."

But even with these words of praise, Satyakāma spoke humbly, "Please, honored Sir, teach me about the nature of Brahman." For Satyakāma wanted to learn from his teacher about the true nature of Brahman.

"You have heard that east and west are Brahman, that the earth and sky are Brahman, that the sun and moon are Brahman, and that the eye and ear are Brahman," his teacher replied. "Like waves stirring within the ocean, all these are a part of Brahman. This is because Brahman is everywhere. Brahman is everything (*Brahmaivedaṃ sarvam*). It is endless. It is the light of life. Everything finds its rest in Brahman.

"And Brahman is realized by knowing the Self, your true nature. Then you realize that you are everywhere—you are endless, and you are radiant. This is the supreme knowledge, Brahma Vidyā. Yes, this is the supreme knowledge, Brahma Vidyā."

And that is how through meditation and knowledge Satyakāma came to know Brahman, and grew up himself to become a great teacher of Brahman.

सर्वं खल्विदं ब्रह्म

Sarvaṃ khalv idaṃ brahma

All this is Brahman—Totality.

Chhāndogya Upanishad, 3.14.1

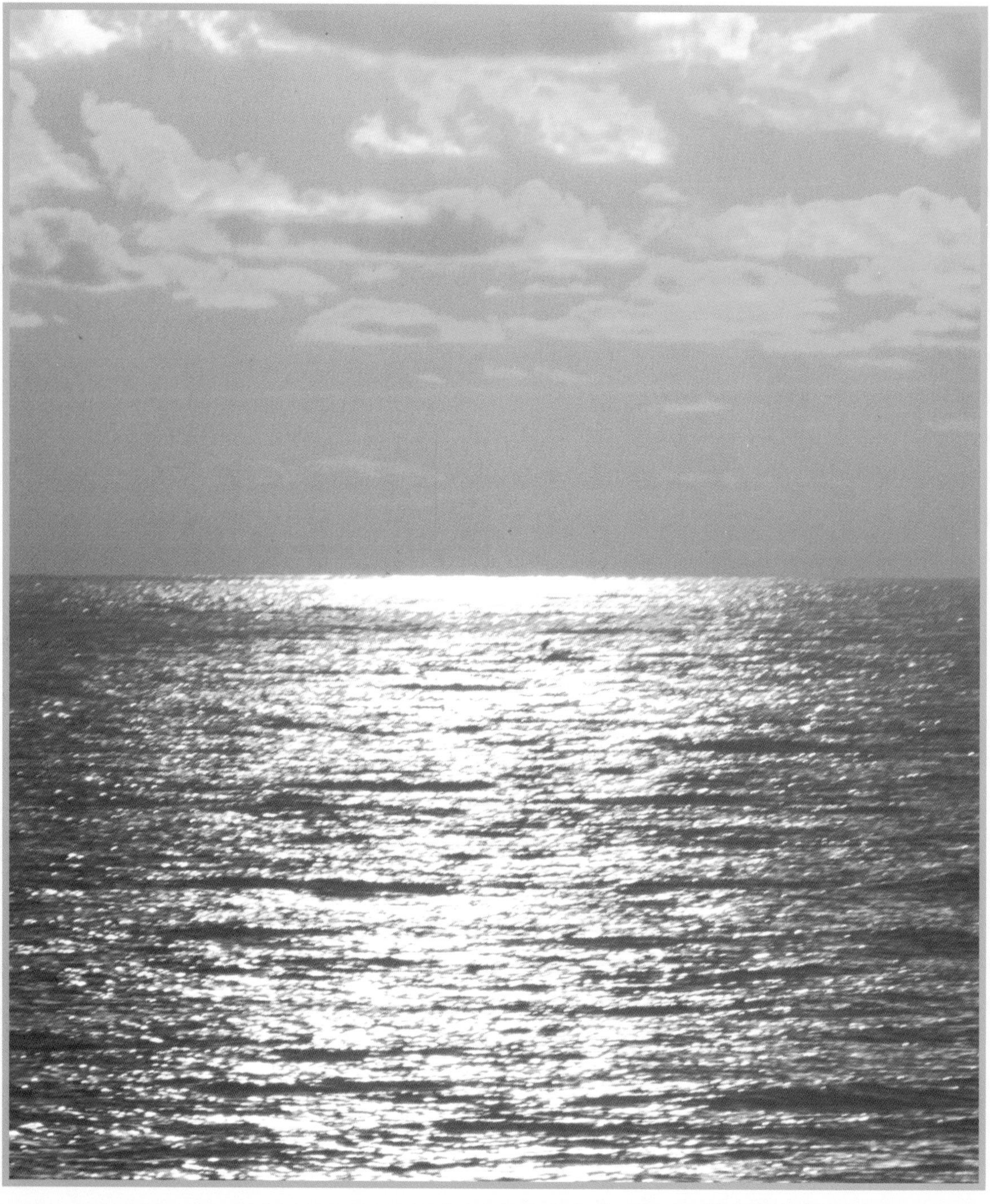

THE STORY OF SHVETAKETU

From the Chhāndogya Upanishad

Many years ago in a village in India there lived a boy named Shvetaketu. Shvetaketu was the son of a great and wise man, Uddālaka.

When Shvetaketu turned twelve, his father said to him, "My dear son, follow the tradition of our family and become a man of knowledge." And so, as was the custom then, Shvetaketu went to the home of his teacher to study.

After many years, he finished his studies and returned to his father's house. His father noticed that something was different about his son Shvetaketu. Shvetaketu thought he knew everything there was to know.

Shvetaketu's father saw his son's pride. "My dear son," he

asked, "I wonder if you have learned the wisdom of the Veda. Can you hear what cannot be heard by the ear? Can you see what cannot be seen by the eyes? Do you know what cannot be known by the mind?"

"What do you mean, dear Father?" asked Shvetaketu in surprise.

"Do you know that by knowing which everything else becomes known?" asked his father.

"What is this teaching, Father?" asked Shvetaketu.

"My son, when you know one lump of clay, you know all that is made of clay.

"When you know one nugget of gold, you know all that is made of gold.

"When you know one pair of iron tongs, you know all that is made of iron."

"I have not yet learned this teaching," said Shvetaketu humbly. "Please, Father, teach me."

"As you wish, my dear son," said his father.

"In the beginning there was an unbounded ocean of consciousness, one without a second (*Ekam evādvitīyam*). The ocean of Being thought to itself, 'I am one—may I be many,' and created light. Light thought to itself, 'I am one—may I be many,' and created water. Water thought to itself, 'I am one—may I be many,' and created matter.

"One unbounded ocean of consciousness became light, water, and matter. And the three became many. In this way the whole universe was created as an unbounded ocean of consciousness ever unfolding within itself.

"That infinite source of the whole universe, the Self of all that is, the ocean of pure consciousness, that essence of all things—that is truth. That is the unbounded Self. Of that you are created. That thou art (*Tat tvam asi*), Shvetaketu."

"Please, honored Sir, tell me more of this teaching," said Shvetaketu.

"As you wish, my dear son," said his father. "Come with me to the orchard."

When they arrived at the orchard, he said, "See the bees collecting nectar? Once the nectar is gathered, it does not say, 'I am the essence of the apple blossom,' or 'I am the essence of the orange blossom.' No, the nectar joins with itself, and is called honey.

"In the same way, Shvetaketu, when people contact the ocean of pure consciousness, they become one with it and do not remember their individual natures. Yet when they are active, they again become a teacher, a farmer, or a goldsmith.

"That subtle essence of the whole world, the Self of all that is, the ocean of pure consciousness—that is truth. That is the eternal Self. Of that you are created. That thou art (*Tat tvam asi*), Shvetaketu."

"Please, honored Sir, teach me more," Shvetaketu said.

"As you wish, my dear boy. Come with me to the river."

When they arrived at the river, they stood at its banks and watched the water rushing by. His father said, "As the rivers flow to the east and merge with the sea, they become the sea itself. Once they are the sea they do not think, 'I am the river Ganges,' or 'I am the river Kshiprā.' They know, 'I am the sea.'

"In the same way, dear Shvetaketu, even though all creatures emerge from the ocean of consciousness, they do not know that. Whatever they are—whether tiger, lion, or wolf—in the end they return to the ocean of consciousness.

"That subtle essence of the whole world, the Self of all that is, the ocean of pure consciousness—that is truth. That is the Self, which unifies. Of that you are created. That thou art (*Tat tvam asi*), Shvetaketu."

"Please, dear Father, teach me still more," Shvetaketu said.

"As you wish, my son," said his father. "Bring me a fruit from the banyan tree."

Shvetaketu went outside and picked a fig from the long branches of the banyan tree. "Here it is, Father," said Shvetaketu.

"Break it open," said his father. "Tell me, what do you see inside?"

"I see many seeds."

"Break one seed open," said his father. "Tell me what you see."

"I see nothing at all," said Shvetaketu.

"My son, that 'nothing' is the subtle essence of all living things, which appears as nothing because you cannot perceive it. But from that nothing this great and ancient tree has grown.

"That infinite source of the whole universe, the Self of all that is, the ocean of pure consciousness—that is truth. That is the unmanifest Self. Of that you are created. That thou art (*Tat tvam asi*), Shvetaketu."

"Please, honored Sir, teach me more," said Shvetaketu.

"As you wish, my dear son," said his father. "Fill this glass with water and add some salt. Then bring it to me in the morning."

Shvetaketu did this. The next morning his father said, "Bring me the salt you poured into the glass."

Shvetaketu returned with the glass of water and said, "The

salt has disappeared, Father."

"Please take a sip from the top of the glass," his father said. "How does it taste?"

"Salty."

"Now pour out some and take a sip from the middle," said his father. "How does it taste?"

"It tastes salty."

"Now pour out some and take a sip from the bottom. Tell me, how does it taste?"

"Salty," said Shvetaketu.

"Even though you couldn't see it, the salt was found in every drop of water. In the same way, pure consciousness is found in all beings. That subtle essence of the whole world, the Self of all that is, the ocean of pure consciousness—that is truth. That is the all-pervading Self. Of that you are created. That thou art (*Tat tvam asi*), Shvetaketu."

"Please, honored Sir, teach me more."

"As you wish, my dear son," said his father. "Think of a man left blindfolded in a desert. He wanders around, not knowing where to go. But if someone removes the blindfold and points out the right direction, he finds his way until finally he reaches home. In the same way, if a teacher points the way to Self-knowledge, then you enjoy the path to enlightenment—from the very first step you grow in intelligence, happiness, and success in life.

"That subtle essence of the whole world, the Self of all that is, the ocean of pure consciousness—that is truth. That is the Self, which removes the darkness of ignorance. Of that you are created. That thou art (*Tat tvam asi*), Shvetaketu.

"When you have known this subtle essence of life, then you have seen the unseen and known the unknown. You have known that by knowing which everything else becomes known."

And then Shvetaketu understood the true teaching of the Veda. Even when he later became a famous teacher in the court of King Janaka, Shvetaketu always remained humble, once he had realized the Self, the ocean of pure consciousness.

अथ यदतः परो दिवो ज्योतिर्दीप्यते विश्वतः पृष्ठेषु
सर्वतः पृष्ठेष्वनुत्तमेषूत्तमेषु लोकेषु
इदं वाव तद्यदिदमस्मिन्नन्तः पुरुषे ज्योतिः

Atha yad ataḥ paro divo jyotir dīpyate vishvataḥ pṛishtheshu
sarvataḥ pṛishtheshv anuttameshūttameshu lokeshu
idaṃ vāva tad yad idam asminn antaḥ purushe jyotiḥ

There is a light which shines beyond the world,
beyond everything, beyond all, beyond the highest heaven.
This is the light which shines within your heart.

Chhāndogya Upanishad, 3.13.7

NACHIKETA GAINS IMMORTALITY

From the Katha Upanishad

Once there was a young boy named Nachiketa, who had many good qualities. He was intelligent, happy, and patient. His wise and peaceful heart shone like the full moon on a clear night.

One day his father, Vājashravas, began a certain *yagya* (a performance that creates balance in nature). Nachiketa felt his heart swell in happiness as the *pandits* (Vedic scholars) offered milk, ghee, and rice. The fire burned brighter and brighter as they chanted the Vedic hymns in a gentle rhythm that was as old as time itself.

After the yagya, Nachiketa watched his father present gifts to the pandits—cotton shawls, mangoes from their garden, and many cows.

As he looked more closely at the cows his father was giving away, the observant Nachiketa suddenly felt worried.

"Unfortunately," he thought, "these cows are weak and thin, and have no more milk. What will happen to the person who gives such poor old cows? Why did my father select his worst cows? Shouldn't he give the plump ones with lots of milk in their udders?"

So the respectful Nachiketa thought to offer himself as a gift. He said to his father, "To whom will you give me?"

Vājashravas realized what his son was saying, but ignored him.

"Father, to whom will you give me?" Nachiketa asked again.

Still his father did not answer. By this time his head was swelling with anger, for he knew his son was pointing out his own lack of generosity.

"To whom will you give me, dear Father?" Nachiketa persisted.

Finally his father burst out, "Unto Yama I give you!"

Nachiketa knew in his heart that his father loved him dearly and that he had only spoken these words in anger.

"My dear son, I do not really wish you to go to Yama," his father said. But though Vājashravas tried to take them back, the obedient Nachiketa felt he should honor his father's words.

So Nachiketa went south to the world of Yama, the administrator of death and immortality. There Nachiketa found Yama's house, surrounded by palm trees and an iron fence.

Yama was not at home. So Nachiketa sat on the doorstep and waited. He waited and waited, and still no sign of Yama. Nachiketa, who was very patient, waited there for three days and three nights. He had no food to eat or water to drink, and no bed to sleep in.

Finally, Nachiketa saw Yama approaching, riding on a water buffalo. On his head Yama wore a golden crown, showing everyone that he rules his own world. He wore red robes and his skin was gray. His eyes glittered like cool gems above his long black mustache.

Yama looked fierce even to the brave Nachiketa. But when Yama started to speak, he smiled and greeted the boy kindly.

"What is such a bright, healthy young man doing on my doorstep?" he asked in surprise.

Nachiketa explained all about his father and the weak cows.

"And you have waited for three days and three nights without eating a morsel or drinking a drop or sleeping a wink!" exclaimed Yama.

Yama was very worried. He knew that he should have treated his young guest better. He remembered the saying, *Atithi devo bhava*—"Honor the guest as God."

Yama wanted to make up for his lack of hospitality. So he said, "Nachiketa, my honored guest, you may have three boons. Ask for three wishes, whatever you want, and be gone."

"For my first wish," Nachiketa answered, "I would like my father's anger to disappear, and I would like him not to worry about me. I would like him to be happy to see me, once I am set free by you."

"As you wish, Nachiketa," Yama replied. "Your father will sleep peacefully through the nights, and will greet you with joy. Choose your second boon."

Nachiketa thought for a while. Then he said, "O Yama, please describe the yagya which will help me reach heaven."

Yama then taught Nachiketa each detail for performing the yagya. Yama taught him the size of the bricks, how to build the altar, and the Vedic hymns to recite. Yama taught Nachiketa how to sprinkle the water, what to offer to the fire, and how to make the offerings while saying *svāhā*, "Hail!"

The clear-minded Nachiketa repeated everything exactly as he had been taught. Yama was pleased with him and said, "From now on, this yagya will be known as the Nāchiketa Fire, in honor of your devotion to knowledge."

Then Yama said, "Choose your third and final boon, O Nachiketa."

"O Yama, teach me the nature of immortality," Nachiketa said. "If I gain immortality, will I still be myself after I die? Or will I become one with the ocean and sky and earth?"

"O Nachiketa, even the *Devas*, even the powers of nature, have doubt on this point," Yama replied in a worried voice. "It is not easy for someone so young to understand, so subtle is this truth. Choose another boon. Release me from this obligation. Do not press me!"

Nachiketa remained steadfast. "No other boon is the equal of this. Please, Sir, instruct me on this point."

"Choose children and grandchildren," Yama begged. "Choose cattle, horses, elephants, and carts filled with gold. Choose vast tracts of land, choose long life for yourself, choose fame, choose swift chariots and dance and song. But do not ask for this, O Nachiketa!"

The wise Nachiketa shook his head. He wanted more than these material things. "Please, Sir, teach me about the mystery beyond human life. Tell me about the nature of immortality. I ask for no other boon."

"You are very intelligent, Nachiketa," Yama finally said, "to choose knowledge instead of worldly things. I will grant you this boon. Here is the secret of immortality."

Then Yama began his instruction: "There are two paths in life—the path of pleasure and the path of spirituality. The first is ignorance and the second is wisdom. They are very different and lead to very different ends.

"The person who seeks pleasure is left with nothing in the end. The one who seeks spirituality obtains Brahman—the totality, the fulfillment of all desires. He rejoices, having attained the source of joy.

"Through a tranquil mind one realizes the Self, which is set in the heart of every creature. This is Brahman, finer than the finest and greater than the greatest (*Anoranīyān mahatomahīyān*)."

"Tell me more about the Self, O Yama, so that I may understand," Nachiketa said.

"You have seen the chariots of the king?" asked Yama.

"Yes," replied Nachiketa.

"Imagine that your body is the chariot, your intellect is the charioteer, and your mind is the reins," Yama said. "Your senses are the horses, and the objects you see in front of you are the roads. The Self is like the lord of the chariot, who rides in back.

"When your intellect (the charioteer) chooses rightly, then the reins stay taut and the horses act like good horses. You can reach your goal easily in such a chariot.

"But when your intellect chooses wrongly, then the reins come loose, and the horses act like wild horses. You will never reach your destination in such a chariot.

"If a person does not know the Self, then his mind is restless, like uncontrolled reins. The horses dash this way and that, dragging the whole chariot in every direction. Such a person never reaches the goal of life.

"But those who know the Self have even minds. They reach their home. They peacefully come to the end of their journey—Brahman."

"Please, Sir, tell me more," Nachiketa said.

"Beyond the objects of perception are the senses," Yama said. "Beyond the senses is the mind, which thinks. Beyond the mind is the intellect, which decides. Beyond the intellect is Ātmā, the Self. The Self is without sound, without touch, and without form.

"The Self is eternal—without beginning or end. By knowing the Self, you know the secret of immortality.

"When you seek life eternal, you must turn your attention inward. There you will find the Self. The innermost Self resides in the center of the heart like a flame without smoke. It is the same today and will be the same tomorrow. It grants all desires.

"The Self is Brahman. It is the immortal. You will know the Self when your senses are still, your mind is at peace, and your heart is pure."

Nachiketa was very grateful to Yama for teaching him. He said, "Thank you, Sir, for this knowledge. Please tell me, what should I do first?"

"Start by knowing that the Self exists," Yama said. "Then seek to learn more about it by experiencing it directly through meditation. When thought has ceased, and even the intellect does not stir, this is the highest state. This is *Yoga*, the state of union.

"Through meditation, you will keep your heart pure and your mind peaceful.

"O Nachiketa, come to know your inner Self, which dwells in your heart. It should be firmly drawn out, as one draws out the air from the center of a reed. This is the pure. This is the immortal. Yes, this is the pure. This is the immortal."

And so the young but wise Nachiketa received from Yama the teaching of immortality and the way to achieve it. After returning to his father, he was freed from all impurities and obtained immortality. He attained Brahman. And so may anyone who truly knows the Self.

अणोरणीयान्महतोमहीयान्

Aṇoraṇīyān mahatomahīyān

Finer than the finest, greater than the greatest.

Katha Upanishad, 1.2.20

TENDERS

RAIKVA THE CART DRIVER

From the Chhāndogya Upanishad

Long ago there was a great king named Jānashruti. His name meant "celebrated among the people." It was a fitting name, because he gave abundantly to all in his kingdom. King Jānashruti invited his subjects to lavish feasts, where he filled long banquet tables with delectable curries, baskets of sweets, and cool drinks.

In each village the king built fountains and lakes surrounded by beautiful gardens. He built smooth roads with rest houses where people traveling on a long journey could eat and spend the night.

"Everyone enjoys my food!" he thought. King Jānashruti liked giving to the people, for he felt that he received many blessings from his generosity.

One evening King Jānashruti was enjoying the cool night air on the marble verandah of his palace. Palm trees and sweet-smelling orchids surrounded the royal silk couch of the wise Jānashruti. A large jade statue of Ganesh, the remover of obstacles, brought good fortune to the famous king.

King Jānashruti rested on his couch and sipped warm milk and ghee (clarified butter) while his chief minister reviewed the day's reports from around the kingdom. The just king prided himself in governing all with fairness.

"We should like to have some fresh mangoes!" he said. Of course, when King Jānashruti made a request, everyone responded quickly, because he was the king, and also because they loved their kind ruler.

As the king relaxed on the verandah, the sun slipped below the horizon, and pink and orange clouds floated in the sky. In the distance, two geese flew gracefully toward the royal palace. The king watched the two geese glide nearer and nearer. As they came closer, the king could not help overhearing them talk to each other.

"Hey ho! Are you blind?" the first goose called to the other. "You must be careful not to fly across this stretch of sky. It is radiant with the splendor of the great-hearted King Jānashruti. Avoid flying through it, or you'll burn your wings!"

King Jānashruti listened contentedly from the marble verandah. He was glad to hear that even the birds knew of his generosity and wisdom.

Then he heard the second goose say, "Who are you talking about? You speak of his brilliance as if he were Raikva."

"Who is this Raikva?" asked the first goose.

"You know how in a game of dice, the winner, the one with the highest throw, takes all?" said the second goose. "Like that, the good deeds that everyone performs all over the kingdom flow to Raikva, because he is the wisest of all. He is the most generous. He gives the most to the people, and he receives the blessings of their good deeds." Then the geese flew away.

King Jānashruti couldn't believe his ears! How could someone else be wiser than himself? Wasn't he the most generous in the land? Who was Raikva, anyway? The king was so upset he barely slept that night in the royal chambers.

As on every other morning, the royal courtiers heralded the new day by singing the praises of the wise and generous king, "O Friend of All the World, we hail you! O Fountain of Glory, we...."

Before they could finish, the king raised his hand and called out to the royal bards, "I cannot bear to hear your praises." Then he said quietly to his attendant, "On this morning I must know—who is Raikva?"

His faithful servant bowed and replied, "Your kind Majesty, I am very sorry, but I have never heard of Raikva. Who is this man?"

King Jānashruti told him about the conversation between the

two geese. "Please search for Raikva," the king said. "I must meet him. Perhaps you will find him on the bank of a river, in a cool cave, or by the peaceful woods."

That day a delegation from the king began a great search for Raikva. They traveled to serene places where saffron-clad holy men with trident staffs practiced their meditations. They walked the banks of sacred rivers, lit the insides of dark caves, and searched the dense forests of the kingdom. But they could not find him among the *yogīs* and wise men.

Finally, the delegation gave up. On their way back to the royal palace, they stopped to rest in the crowded marketplace of a small village. The market was bursting with people and overflowing with food.

Mangoes, bananas, coconuts, dates, guavas, and papayas were piled high on wooden ox-carts in the cramped market. Mounds of *tīka* powder in red, pink, and yellow formed colorful pyramids on the traders' mats.

"Come repair your sandals!" cried the shoe *wallah* (vendor).

"Only one *rupee* for a shave!" called out the barber from his stall.

"Two rupees to hem your *dhotī* (clothing)!" called the tailor from his shop.

Vendors fried *samosās* (spicy vegetables) and *pūrīs* (puffed bread) in vats of clarified butter. The pungent aroma of spices popping in ghee mingled with the sweet smell of hanging marigold and jasmine garlands.

Rickshaws darted in and out among the crowd. Goats and pigs wandered through the streets looking for food. The rooftops teemed with monkeys scampering and screeching, as if chattering about the high price of bananas. White cows napped safely in the middle of the street, flower blossoms adorning their painted horns.

Amidst the noise and din, the king's representatives sat drinking fresh juice from tender coconut shells. They were very tired, and the bustling marketplace made them feel more exhausted than ever.

As they sat, they noticed a man sitting in the shade under a bullock cart. His clothes were in rags, and his feet were dusty.

Even though he looked like a poor man, his large serene eyes and peaceful face created a feeling of silence amidst the clatter of the market. A radiant light shone all around him. He seemed to be floating in sweet, simple happiness.

"That man looks like a great Ṛishi, a great seer, from the Himālayas!" exclaimed one of the king's men.

He walked over to the man sitting under the cart and said, "Excuse me. Are you Raikva?"

"Yes, I am," the man replied with a radiant smile.

The king's delegation forgot their tiredness. They felt jubilant and happy. They rushed back to the palace.

"Your Majesty, we have found him!" they proclaimed as they entered the royal court.

King Jānashruti was delighted, and decided that he himself would pay a visit to Raikva. He said, "I will meet this man tomorrow! I will bring him many expensive gifts!"

The king thought he would please Raikva with his generosity. Leading a grand parade of mighty elephants, strong soldiers, and beautiful chariots, the king left the palace and marched toward the small village where Raikva lived.

The villagers heralded King Jānashruti with the fanfare of trumpets and blaring of conches. "*Jai Rājā*! Hail the King! *Jai Rājā*!" the people chanted as the king passed by on his gold and red palanquin (covered chair), resting on the shoulders of four attendants. Never before had the glorious King Jānashruti come to their village.

As the king entered the marketplace, he stepped out of his palanquin and stood up. The crowd cheered louder, but when he held up his hand for silence, not a whisper stirred among them.

As the villagers stared in disbelief, the king carried garlands of jasmine and marigolds to the bullock cart where the serene Raikva was sitting. Even the sleeping cows looked up to see what was happening.

"Greetings, O revered Raikva!" cried the king, for all to hear. "I wish to bestow upon you a gold necklace and a chariot. Choose six hundred cows from the royal herd. The royal court this day smiles upon you! Good fortune has come to you! Today these precious goods are yours!"

The king was sure that the poor Raikva would be overwhelmed with his precious gifts. But Raikva did not even look at them. He looked straight at the proud king. "I don't want your gifts," he said gently. "Please take them and leave."

Everyone gasped. No one had ever refused the king's gifts before. What would happen now?

The king said nothing. He simply returned to his palanquin and—with his mighty elephants, strong soldiers, and beautiful chariots—slowly rode back to the royal palace in silence.

Sad and dejected, the king closed himself in his royal chambers so that he could be alone to think. "What went wrong?" he wondered. "Why didn't the poor Raikva accept my gifts?"

The king remembered Raikva's serene eyes and peaceful face.

He thought about his radiant light. He thought about Raikva's gentle smile. He thought and thought.

Suddenly the king knew what went wrong.

He realized that the gifts he offered—cows and gold—meant nothing to Raikva. Raikva owned inner happiness. Raikva owned spiritual knowledge. Raikva owned peace, simplicity, and bliss. The king saw that he himself owned only marble and gems.

"Raikva's spiritual happiness is much more valuable than my material gifts," thought the king. "All that I have means nothing to Raikva. But what Raikva has means everything to me!"

Then the king knew he must return to Raikva.

Once again the king set out—with his mighty elephants, strong soldiers, and beautiful chariots—to visit the peaceful Raikva. This time the king would offer even more gold, cows, and chariots. But this time giving gifts was no longer important to the king. This time he went with humility.

Arriving in the village, the king bowed down to Raikva and

said quietly, "Dear Sir, I humbly ask you to keep these gifts. What I wish with all my heart is for you to accept me as your student. Please Sir, teach me what true happiness is."

This time Raikva accepted the king's gifts. He saw that King Jānashruti had lost his pride, and was ready to learn. He saw that the king sincerely wanted knowledge.

And so Raikva taught the king the nature of Ātmā, the Self. "The Self does not need anything," he said. "It is fulfilled and self-sufficient. He who knows the Self finds bliss. He finds satisfaction. His happiness lasts forever.

"If you know the real nature of the Self, you will never want anything. You will always be content."

Raikva then taught the king about giving. "Dear King," he said, "it is good that you like to help others, but do not give with pride. Remember that the things you give away are not yours. They are gifts from nature. Give them in all humility.

"And while it is good to give material possessions to the people, it is better to give spiritual welfare. Knowing the unbounded Self will make the people truly happy. Yes, this will make them happy."

Then Raikva taught the king how to practice meditation, which is the heart of the Vedic tradition of knowledge. The king was grateful to receive Raikva's gifts, and he returned to his palace.

The king practiced meditation each morning as the sun rose over his marble verandah and each evening as it set. He felt more peaceful and content each day.

One day he thought, "I want to give the people what I feel inside. I want to give them what Raikva gave me. I want to give them true happiness."

And so the king asked that all his subjects be taught meditation. After a short while, his people began to awaken early in the morning, feeling fresh and vital.

The people became more energetic and creative. Crime and sickness disappeared. They built beautiful homes and cities, and turned their kingdom into a garden. They celebrated festivals with singing and dancing. The heavens blessed the crops with rain. Cows gave plenty of fresh milk, beehives overflowed with honey, and trees bowed low with fruit. People easily followed their *Dharma*, their natural duty. They enjoyed satisfaction and contentment and lived their daily lives in bliss.

King Jānashruti became known as a great king, a *Mahārāja*, a truly spiritual king who had found real fulfillment within himself, and taught his subjects how to know true happiness.

Thanks to the wise King Jānashruti, the entire kingdom enjoyed Heaven on Earth.

योो वै भूमा तत्सुखं नाल्पे सुखमस्ति

Yo vai bhūmā tat sukhaṃ nālpe sukham asti

That which is unbounded is happy.
There is no happiness in the small.

Chhāndogya Upanishad, 7.23

INDRA ASKS ABOUT THE SELF

From the Chhāndogya Upanishad

High in the starry heavens Prajāpati, the protector of life, was teaching about the nature of Ātmā, the Self.

"Ātmā is free from wrong, free from sorrow, free from hunger and thirst," he said. "Those who know Ātmā fulfill all their desires. They gain all worlds. If you want to know the truth, you should know the true nature of Ātmā, the Self."

Prajāpati's words were overheard by both the shining *Devas* (the positive powers of nature) and the *asuras* (the negative powers). Both the Devas and the asuras thought, "We must learn about Ātmā, the Self. It is through the Self that we will gain support from nature. By knowing the Self, we can fulfill all our desires."

So each group sent a representative to find out the nature of Ātmā from Prajāpati. The Devas sent Indra, their glorious leader, who wields the mighty thunderbolt. The asuras sent Virochana to represent them.

"Please, Sir, tell us the true nature of Ātmā, the Self," Indra and Virochana humbly asked Prajāpati.

"Bring a pan of water," said Prajāpati.

They brought a pan of water. "When you look into the water, what do you see?" Prajāpati asked.

"We see our faces and bodies, even our hair and nails," they answered.

"This is Ātmā," said Prajāpati. "This is the immortal. This is the spirit. This is the Self."

Upon hearing this, Indra and Virochana went home with peaceful hearts, thinking they had learned the nature of Ātmā. As they left, Prajāpati looked at them and thought, "They go away without having known the Self. They think that the body is the Self. Whoever thinks such a thing will not become enlightened."

After the meeting, Virochana went triumphantly back to the asuras and told them, "The body is Ātmā. If the body is satisfied, then we will obtain all our desires." They were very happy to have this teaching.

Indra, on the other hand, felt confused. He was driving his golden chariot across the sky, turning over in his mind the words Prajāpati had spoken. He did not even notice the jeweled palaces, golden rivers, or lotus lakes he passed over. Suddenly, he stopped his chariot in mid-air.

"Wait a minute!" he thought. "Something seems to be wrong here. If the Self is the body, then the Self must die when the body dies. Therefore, the Self would not be immortal."

Indra decided to go back to Prajāpati, to find out more about Ātmā, the Self. Indra said, "Please, Sir, teach me more about the true nature of the Self."

Prajāpati was pleased with Indra's request. "O Maghavan, O

Indra, he who plays happily in a dream, he is Ātmā. He is the Self. He is pure happiness," Prajāpati said. With this answer, Indra left with a peaceful heart.

Indra started driving his golden chariot across the sky to bring the Devas this answer—that the person who dreams is the Self. Along the way, he started to think about Prajāpati's words. He did not even notice the blue-tinted mountains, still pools, or singing waterfalls he flew over. Suddenly, he stopped his chariot in mid-air.

"Wait a minute!" he thought. "The person who dreams can also experience unhappiness. He can have a bad dream. Surely this is not Ātmā. Surely this is not the Self, which is pure happiness."

Indra decided to return once again to Prajāpati, to find out more about Ātmā. "Please, Sir, teach me more about the true nature of the Self," he said.

Again Prajāpati was pleased with Indra's request. "O Maghavan," Prajāpati said, "when a person is asleep, still and tranquil, and is not dreaming, that is the Self. That is Ātmā. That is fulfillment." With this answer, Indra left with a peaceful heart.

Indra began driving back to the other Devas with this answer—that the person who sleeps is the Self. Along the way, he started to think about Prajāpati's words. He did not even notice the drowsy sun slipping behind the hills, the cool twilight wind weaving the air, or the soothing call of evening birds far below him. Suddenly he stopped his chariot in mid-air.

"Wait a minute!" he thought. "The person who sleeps is not even aware that he is sleeping. How can he be fulfilled?"

Again Indra returned to Prajāpati to find out more about Ātmā. Folding his hands in respect, Indra patiently asked, "Please, Sir, teach me more about the true nature of the Self."

Prajāpati at last told Indra the true meaning of Ātmā. "O Maghavan, the body is mortal. But the Self is immortal—it lives forever. While associated with the body, the Self experiences pleasure and pain. When the Self is no longer associated with the body, it goes beyond pleasure and pain. The Self remains always the same. The Self is immortal.

"You have seen the sky?" asked Prajāpati.

"Yes, Revered Teacher," answered Indra.

"The sky is formless and shapeless," continued Prajāpati, "but for a time it takes on the shape of clouds, lightning, or thunder. These appear and then vanish. The sky remains the same. Just like clouds, our bodies appear and then vanish. And like the sky, the Self remains the same. The Self is immortal.

"For a time, the Self becomes as if hidden by the golden world. It is said, 'The face of truth is hidden by a covering of gold' (*Hiraṇmayena pātreṇa satyasyāpihitaṃ mukham*). But then the Self shines through, because the Self is immortal.

"When the Self knows its own nature, it shines within itself. This is the highest light. This is Ātmā. When the Self knows its own nature, it laughs and plays and rejoices. The Self is pure happiness. The Self is immortal."

Then Prajāpati asked, "You have seen how the water buffalo is attached to the cart?"

"Yes, Sir," answered Indra.

"Just like that, the Self is joined to the body," continued Prajāpati. "The water buffalo is not always attached to the cart, however. Sometimes it plays in pools of water, and sometimes it wanders in the fields eating grass. Like this, the Self becomes free. Established in the Self, one is eternally happy.

"When you look at the sky, O Indra, your eyes do the seeing, but the Self is the seer. This is why we say, 'I see the sky.' When you smell jasmine, your nose does the smelling, but the Self is the one who smells jasmine. This is why we say, 'I smell the jasmine.'

"When you speak, O Indra, your voice does the speaking, but the Self is the speaker. This is why we say, 'I am speaking.' When you listen to music, your ears do the hearing, but the Self is the listener. This is why we say, 'I hear the music.' It is the Self who is the enjoyer of bliss. It is the Self who is fulfilled."

Indra smiled and thanked Prajāpati. Then Indra returned to the Devas and told them what he had learned about the Self,

Ātmā. All together, they meditated, and came to know the true nature of the Self as immortal, as pure happiness, as fulfillment. Therefore the Devas achieved all their desires, and they obtained all worlds. Yes, they achieved all their desires, and obtained all worlds. And so can anyone who knows the Self.

तरति शोकमात्मवित्

Tarati shokam ātmavit

Established in the Self, one overcomes sorrows and suffering.

Chhāndogya Upanishad, 7.1.3

THE DEVAS AND THE BLADE OF GRASS

From the Kena Upanishad

On the edge of a great forest long ago, the morning sun warmed the walls of a quiet āshram (Vedic school). Many young students lived there in tidy thatched cottages. Every day children sat under the spreading branches of an ancient banyan tree and recited the Vedic texts after their teacher.

One morning, after the students had finished their meditations, they gathered on the soft, cool grass under the tree. Sunlight flickered and danced through the lacy canopy of leaves, casting a kaleidoscope of designs on the students' yellow cotton *kurtās* (traditional long shirts). They chattered happily to each other, waiting for their *āchārya*, their great teacher, to give the morning's lesson.

The āchārya appeared at the door of his cottage. His eyes sparkled like the warm and gentle morning sun. His sandals whispered in the grass as he walked. The students stood and folded their hands to greet him. After he sat down, the children gathered around and sat on the grass at his feet.

The teacher began his lesson with a blessing:

"May our arms and legs be strong.
May our speech be full of life,
and also our breath, eyes, and ears.
May all our senses be healthy and strong.
Āpyāyantu mamāngāni
vāk prāṇash chakshuḥ shrotram
atho balam indriyāṇi cha sarvāṇi

"Everything is Brahman—this is the greatest teaching.
May we always uphold Brahman.

May Brahman always uphold us.
May we abide in Brahman.
May Brahman abide in us.
Let this great truth delight in us
and live in us,
and awaken the Self."

Sarvaṃ brahmopanishadaṃ
māham brahma nirākuryāṃ
mā mā brahma nirākarot
anirākaraṇam astu
anirākaraṇaṃ me 'stu
tad ātmani nirate ya upanishatsu
dharmās te mayi santu
te mayi santu

"This morning you will learn the secret of Brahman," said the āchārya. "And we will start with your questions." A murmur of excitement rippled through the group, because the children loved secrets. And even more than that, they loved to ask questions.

One of the older students eagerly started by asking, "*Kena*?" which means "by whom?"

"By whom does the mind think?" he asked his teacher. "By whom do the eyes see and the ears hear? By whose desire does life begin to move? By whose wish does a person begin to speak?"

The āchārya thought for a moment, looking at both the older and younger students. He decided to speak to the older students first.

"The answer is Brahman, which is wholeness," he said. "Brahman is the ear of the ear, and the mind of the mind. It is the breath of the breath, and the eye of the eye.

"Brahman cannot be expressed by speech, but it is that by which we are able to speak.

"Brahman cannot be thought by the mind, but it is that by which the mind thinks.

"Brahman cannot be seen by the eyes, but it is that by which the eyes see.

"Brahman cannot be heard by the ears, but it is that by which the ears hear."

The āchārya continued, "When someone really knows Brahman, he finds truth, and that fortunate person becomes immortal. He lives forever. If, however, a person does not know Brahman, then his life is a great loss."

The teacher noticed that the younger students looked confused. They were saying with their eyes, "We don't understand what you mean!" So he decided to tell them a story. This is what he said—

At the beginning of time a vast ocean of milk covered the entire universe. The creamy ocean covered all that was. In the middle of this ocean towered a great mountain.

Vishnu, who maintains the creation, told the Devas (the positive powers of nature) how to churn the ocean so they could become immortal. "Take rare and precious herbs and throw them into the ocean," he said. "Use the mountain to stir the waters. Then you will receive the nectar of immortality, *amṛitam*."

The asuras (the negative powers) also wanted the nectar of immortality, so they joined the Devas. Together they tied giant ropes to the mountain, and pulled on the ropes. First the Devas pulled in one direction. Then the asuras pulled in the opposite direction. They turned the mountain harder and harder, faster and faster. Together they churned, like butter, the bottomless ocean of milk.

As they churned the ocean, many wonderful things emerged from the top of the mountain. Out came Dhanvantari, the first physician, dressed in white robes and holding in his hand a golden vessel, called a *kalash*.

This vessel, everyone knew, contained within it the precious nectar of immortality, amṛitam. Both the Devas and the asuras badly wanted the amṛitam, because they wanted to live forever.

They wanted this more than they wanted anything else. Before anyone could stop them, the asuras suddenly snatched the kalash and raced across the sky with the prized amṛitam.

The Devas chased the asuras through the heavens. As they raced across the sky, four drops of nectar spilled out from the kalash. The four places where these drops fell later became the sites of large festivals, which have been celebrated for millennia in India. The largest of these festivals, held every twelve years in Allahabad, is called the *Kumbha Melā* and attracts millions of seekers even today.

The Devas fought a great battle with the asuras to win back the amṛitam. The battle lasted for thousands of years, but sadly, after some time, it appeared that the Devas were losing.

The sun and moon, the planets and stars watched anxiously from their homes high in the starry sky. They realized that the Devas could never win without help from the strongest power of all—Brahman. All of nature begged Brahman to rescue the Devas.

Just when it seemed that the Devas would surely lose, Brahman finally came to help. It is said that "Truth alone triumphs" (*Satyam eva jayate*), and so with truth on their side, the Devas captured the amṛitam. And that is how the Devas won the war with the asuras and gained immortality.

Unfortunately, instead of honoring Brahman for saving them, the Devas took credit for themselves. "We are so glorious!" they shouted. "We won the battle!"

Brahman saw their pride. He saw that they had forgotten who had won the war for them. So he decided to teach them a lesson.

Brahman appeared in front of the Devas in the form of a spirit. The Devas were baffled. Who was this spirit? What did he want?

They asked Agni (fire), to find out who this mysterious being was.

"Who are you?" the spirit asked as Agni came near.

"I am Agni Jātavedas," Agni replied.

"What power do you have?" the spirit asked.

"I am the great lord of fire," said Agni. "I can scorch everything. I can burn the entire world to ashes with the slightest thought."

"Then burn this," said the spirit, placing a single blade of grass in front of Agni.

Agni howled and rushed in a red blaze toward the blade of grass. With all his strength he flared and flamed, trying to ignite it. But he could not kindle even a spark. Defeated, he returned to the other Devas.

"I could not find out who this spirit is before us," he said humbly.

The Devas then turned to Vāyu (wind). They asked him to find out who the spirit was.

"Who are you?" the spirit asked as Vāyu came near.

"I am Vāyu Mātarishvan," Vāyu replied.

"What is your power?" Brahman (the spirit) asked.

"I am the great lord of wind," Vāyu said. "With a mighty gust of air I can blow away everything in the sky and on earth."

"Then blow this away," said the spirit, placing a single blade of grass in front of Vāyu.

Vāyu spun like a tornado and whirled around the blade of grass. He huffed and puffed a raging blast of air. But he could not move the blade of grass even a fraction of an inch. Defeated, he returned to the other Devas.

"I could not find out who this spirit is before us," he said, dejected.

The Devas then turned to Indra, their leader. "O Indra, find out who this spirit is!"

Mighty Indra in his shining robes and glittering crown went to the same spot. But the spirit had disappeared. In its place stood Umā, the pure and beautiful daughter of the Himālayas, the snow-capped mountains.

"Do you know who that spirit was?" Indra asked her.

"Yes, I know," Umā replied. "It was Brahman. It was because of Brahman that the Devas were victorious in battle. Because of Brahman the eyes see and the ears hear."

Indra now realized that it was Brahman who had won victory for the Devas. He and the other Devas finally admitted that they should not have been so proud. They praised Brahman for their victory and for their happiness.

Having finished the story, the teacher asked his pupils if they understood. "Now do you know by whom the mind thinks?" he asked the youngest. "Do you know by whom the Devas achieved their victory? Do you know 'Kena,' which means 'by whom'? Do you know by whom the eyes see and the ears hear? Do you know who is the eye of the eye and the breath of the breath?"

"Now we know by whom—by Brahman, the wholeness of the Self," answered a student. "By means of Brahman the eyes see and the ears hear. By means of Brahman the Devas received their strength."

The teacher smiled and nodded happily. “Brahman is the goal of all desires—it is the dearest of all,” he said. “You can know Brahman by meditating with a settled mind. When the mind is settled, Brahman dawns like a flash of lightning, like the twinkling of the eyes.

Whoever knows Brahman becomes dear to everyone. Whoever knows Brahman becomes immortal. Now you know the secret. You have been taught the secret teaching of Brahman.”

The students left their seats and, one by one, quietly touched the feet of the teacher. Then the great āchārya stood and walked back to his cottage, his sandals whispering in the grass. The morning’s lesson was over.

ब्रह्मविद् ब्रह्मैव भवति

Brahmavid brahmaiva bhavati

The knower of Brahman is Brahman itself.

Muṇḍaka Upanishad, 3.2.9

YĀGYAVALKYA
THE GREAT TEACHER

From the Bṛihadāraṇyaka Upanishad

In India there was once a great teacher named Yāgyavalkya. He was famous throughout the land for his knowledge and experience of Brahman (wholeness). He lived in a glorious kingdom called Videha, where the people dwelled in perfect health and great happiness.

In Videha the rains came on time and the crops were plentiful. The markets overflowed with mangoes, bananas, oranges, and papayas. This was because the people lived pure lives and the king conducted many yagyas to bring balance in nature.

One year the wealthy and generous king of Videha, King

Janaka, decided to hold a large yagya. He invited all the wisest Brahmins (scholarly teachers) in the kingdom, including the most famous, Yāgyavalkya.

King Janaka himself was a wise person, and was in the habit of honoring the Brahmins by giving them generous gifts. On the day of his great yagya, as he looked at the wise teachers gathered before him, King Janaka suddenly wanted to know who among them was the greatest. Which star was the brightest?

To find out, King Janaka decided to offer a prize. He set aside one thousand cows from the royal herd. From the horns of each cow he hung ten gold coins.

"Most revered Brahmins," he said to the assembled sages, "whoever among you is the wisest, that person may drive home these cows."

No one moved. Each looked at the others in suspense. For sure, the prize was tempting, but who would dare claim the cows? Who would prove to be a superior Vedic scholar in such a meeting of the wise?

The air hung heavy and hot. It was so still they could hear the cows lowing in the distance. Finally, Yāgyavalkya stood up. He said to his young pupil, "Sāmashravas, my dear, drive home those cows." And the young boy took the cows away.

Suddenly everyone was in an uproar. All the other Brahmins cried out, "How can he declare himself the wisest?" To quiet the crowd, King Janaka's chief pandit, Ashvala, approached Yāgyavalkya.

"Are you indeed the wisest among us?" he asked Yāgyavalkya respectfully.

"I bow to the wisest among us," replied Yāgyavalkya, "but I really want those cows."

And so began a great debate to decide who was the greatest teacher, with King Janaka looking on.

Ashvala, Ārtabhāga, Bhujyu, and many other sages stood up to question Yāgyavalkya. Some asked questions about how to perform yagyas. Some asked about the senses, the objects of the senses, and the directions in space. Others asked about the nature of Ātmā (the Self). The debate continued all day, with all the pandits and scholars intent on hearing every word. Each person thought they would be the one to vanquish Yāgyavalkya, yet each was silenced by his brilliant answers.

The sun was slipping low in the sky when the great Vedic scholar Gārgī stood up. "Yāgyavalkya," she said, "My questions are sharp and pointed, like two arrows. What is above heaven, beneath the earth, and yet between the two? What is woven across the past, present, and future?"

"O Gārgī, it is Brahman," Yāgyavalkya answered without hesitating. "Brahman is above heaven, beneath the earth, and yet between the two. Brahman is the same in the past, present, and future.

"Brahman is neither short nor long. It is without taste, without smell, and without hearing. Yet at its command, the sun and moon rise in the east and set in the west, O Gārgī. It commands the endless cycles of the days and nights, the seasons and years.

"Brahman is unseen, but is the seer. It is unheard, but is the hearer. It is unthought, but is the thinker. There is no other seer than this, no other hearer than this, no other knower than this. In it everything is woven, like the warp and woof of cloth. Nothing exists but that (*Neha nānāsti kinchana*)," said Yāgyavalkya.

And so Gārgī, like the others, bowed to Yāgyavalkya. He asked if there were any more questions. No one else dared to speak.

"Whether one offers gifts in yagyas, like King Janaka, or sits still in meditation, the goal of life is to realize Brahman," Yāgyavalkya said.

Then all the wise sages declared Yāgyavalkya to be the greatest teacher, for he showed himself to be the most enlightened in the whole kingdom. King Janaka garlanded him with rose and jasmine blossoms.

And that is how Yāgyavalkya won the thousand cows.

Long after the debate, King Janaka continued to live in his jewel-studded palace with marble floors and sandalwood walls. Known far and wide for his dazzling wealth, King Janaka seemed to enjoy all the happiness life could offer. He and his wife had a beautiful and enlightened daughter named Sītā. The king was just and kind, loved by all the people.

King Janaka was not satisfied, however, with all the riches that life had to offer. He wanted to learn more about Brahman. At that time, no one learned from books. Students learned under the guidance of a teacher, an āchārya. So, one morning, King Janaka called the wise Yāgyavalkya to his court. The king wanted to question him about Brahman.

As Yāgyavalkya entered the golden doors of the court, King Janaka, dressed in shining silk, stood up and smiled. He greeted Yāgyavalkya with hands folded in respect and offered him a high seat of honor. The king asked the attendants to bring water for Yāgyavalkya, and to garland him with jasmine.

"*Namaste*! (Greetings!)" said Yāgyavalkya.

"Namaste!" the king said. "All is well with you?"

"Yes, all is well, Your Majesty," Yāgyavalkya answered.

"O Yāgyavalkya," the king asked, "for what purpose have you come? Have you come to answer my questions or have you come for more cows?"

"For both, Your Majesty!" answered Yāgyavalkya, with a twinkle.

Then Yāgyavalkya said, "If someone were going on a long journey, they would need a fast chariot or a strong ship. Like that, life itself is a long journey and one needs a good mind. You have such a mind, Your Majesty. You are wise to ask subtle questions."

And so the king began to question him.

"My dear Yāgyavalkya," began King Janaka, "by what light does a person see?"

"A person sees by the light of the sun, Your Majesty,"

Yāgyavalkya answered.

"But if the sun has set, by what light does a person see?" King Janaka asked.

"If the sun has set, a person sees by the light of the moon, Your Majesty," answered the great sage.

"If the sun has set and the moon has set, by what light does a person see?" King Janaka asked.

"If the sun has set and the moon has set, a person sees by the light of fire," answered Yāgyavalkya.

"If the sun has set, the moon has set, and the fire has gone out, by what light does a person see?" King Janaka asked.

"If the sun has set, the moon has set, and the fire has gone out, a person sees by the light of the Self."

"If the sun has set, the moon has set, the fire has gone out, and the Self has gone out, by what light does a person see?" King Janaka persisted.

"You ask too many questions!" said Yāgyavalkya. "For the Self never goes out. It never sets. It is eternal. It is the light that shines within the heart, by which a person may always see."

With this King Janaka felt satisfied, having understood that the Self within is the eternal light of Brahman.

"The knower of Brahman is calm, self-controlled, and patient," Yāgyavalkya said. "He sees the Self in all things and all things in the Self. This is the world of Brahman. You have attained this world, Your Majesty. You have attained Brahman."

"I give you the kingdom of Videha," King Janaka said. "I give myself as your servant."

Yāgyavalkya, however, not desiring the kingdom, accepted more cows as a gift and went home.

Many years after teaching King Janaka, Yāgyavalkya decided to leave his life as a householder, and become a forest dweller.

At that time, the ideal length of life was said to be a hundred years, or a hundred long autumns. It was divided into four parts: the first twenty-five years were called *brahmacharya*, or student life; the second twenty-five years *gārhasthya*, householder life; the third twenty-five *vānaprasthya*, forest dweller life; and the last twenty-five *sannyāsa*, retired life.

The ideal of Vedic living was for students to gain enlightenment by the time they were adults, and enjoy an entire lifetime of bliss, fulfillment, and success. Yāgyavalkya had achieved this ideal state of life.

Now in his latter years, Yāgyavalkya called his dear wife, Maitreyī, and said, "My beloved, it is my time of life to become a forest dweller. What would you like me to give to you before I leave? Would you like my wealth?"

"Even if I possessed the wealth of the whole world," Maitreyī asked, "would I become immortal?"

"No, my dear wife, you would not."

"Please, my dear husband," Maitreyī requested, "give me

something that will make me immortal."

"You are truly dear to me, Maitreyī," said Yāgyavalkya. "I will give you knowledge, and this will bring you immortality."

He spoke the following words:

"It is not for the sake of the husband
that the husband is dear,
but for the sake of the Self, Ātmā,
that the husband is dear.

Na vā are patyuḥ kāmāya
patiḥ priyo bhavati
ātmanas tu kāmāya
patiḥ priyo bhavati

"It is not for the sake of the wife
that the wife is dear,
but for the sake of the Self, Ātmā,
that the wife is dear.

Na vā are jāyāyai kāmāya

jāyā priyā bhavati
ātmanas tu kāmāya
jāyā priyā bhavati

"It is not for the sake of the children
that the children are dear,
but for the sake of the Self, Ātmā,
that the children are dear.
Na vā are putrāṇāṃ kāmāya
putrāḥ priyā bhavanti
ātmanas tu kāmāya
putrāḥ priyā bhavanti

"It is not for the sake of everything
that everything is dear,
but for the sake of the Self, Ātmā,
that everything is dear.
Na vā are sarvasya kāmāya
sarvaṃ priyaṃ bhavati

ātmanas tu kāmāya
sarvaṃ priyaṃ bhavati

"The Self should be seen, heard,
contemplated, and realized.
O Maitreyī, when the Self is known,
then everything is known."

Ātmā vā are drashtavyaḥ shrotavyo
mantavyo nididhyāsitavyaḥ
Maitreyi ātmano vā are darshanena shravaṇena
matyā vigyānenedaṃ sarvaṃ viditam

After giving Maitreyī the precious knowledge of the Self, Yāgyavalkya asked his wife a question. "My dear, have you noticed that you cannot grasp the sound that comes from a drum?"

"Yes," answered Maitreyī.

"However, if you grasp the drum, you can create the sound that comes out," he said. "In the same way, you cannot catch the tunes that come out of a flute. But when you grasp the flute, you can play it, and thereby create the sounds that come from it.

"Like that, when you know the Self, Ātmā, which is the source of creation, you can create the life that you desire."

And then Yāgyavalkya went to dwell in the forest and further develop his spiritual life. Yāgyavalkya had been an āchārya, a great teacher, teaching the true understanding of the Veda, pure knowledge, which he knew from his own experience. Through his teaching he fulfilled his life's purpose and helped many, many others to reach the goal of life—the experience of infinite bliss—Brahman.

आत्मा वा अरे द्रष्टव्यः श्रोतव्यो
मन्तव्यो निदिध्यासितव्यः

Ātmā vā are drashtavyaḥ shrotavyo
mantavyo nididhyāsitavyaḥ

That Ātmā alone, that state of simplest form of awareness alone, is worthy of seeing, hearing, contemplating, and realizing.

Bṛihadāraṇyaka Upanishad, 2.4.5

BHṚIGU DISCOVERS THE NATURE OF BRAHMAN

From the Taittirīya Upanishad

One day long ago, a small boy named Bhṛigu sat in the shade of a palm tree with his father, Varuṇa. White clouds drifted slowly above fields of rice. Harvesters bent low, sickles flashing in the sun. Water buffalo waded in the shallow waters of the field.

Father and son sat quietly together. "Dear Father," Bhṛigu said, "teach me about Brahman."

"My dear son," Varuṇa said, "I am happy you want to know about Brahman. Do you see the clouds rolling across the sky? Do you see the growers harvesting the plump rice kernels? Do you see the water buffalo wading in the water?"

"Yes, Father," Bhṛigu said.

"All these are composed of matter, breath, sight, hearing, mind, and speech (*annaṃ prāṇaṃ chakshuh shrotraṃ mano vācham*)," his father said.

"That out of which these are born,
that in which they are sustained,
and that to which they go and merge again—
Yato vā imāni bhūtāni jāyante
yena jātāni jīvanti
yat prayanty abhisaṃvishanti

"Seek to know that, O Bhṛigu. That is Brahman. That is wholeness."

"Dear Father, how can I experience Brahman?" asked Bhṛigu.

"You will experience Brahman through meditation *(tapas)*," his father said. "Soon you will be old enough to receive your initiation, *Upanayana*. Then you will learn how to meditate."

Bhṛigu's heart swelled with joy at his father's words. One morning a few weeks later, Bhṛigu's family and friends gathered together for his initiation. Bhṛigu's mother cut his hair and set out new white clothes for him to wear after his bath.

When Bhṛigu entered the courtyard, the pandits (Vedic scholars) were already chanting. As his mother watched with loving eyes, Bhṛigu approached his father, his hands folded to show respect. Together Bhṛigu and his father found a place of honor beside the orange-robed pandits, facing the sun. The ground was covered with marigold petals. Incense filled the air.

At the auspicious moment, Varuṇa gently placed the special cotton thread, woven in three strands, over Bhṛigu's left shoulder. He poured water from his own cupped hands into Bhṛigu's hands. He asked Bhṛigu to stand firm on a large rock, steadfast like a steady mind. Varuṇa said,

"All good you should hear from the ears.
All good you should see through the eyes."
Bhadraṃ karṇebhiḥ shṛiṇuyāma devāḥ
bhadraṃ pashyemākshabhir yajatrāḥ

Then Bhṛigu's mother and aunts gave him round, golden sweets, called *laddus*. Finally, after the initiation ceremony was over, Bhṛigu's father took him to a quiet place and taught him to meditate.

Bhṛigu closed his eyes. At once he felt a deep stirring within his consciousness. Now he knew he would discover the nature of Brahman. His father asked him to practice meditation every morning and afternoon.

That afternoon Bhṛigu waded across the rice field and sat down next to a fast-moving stream. Soon he sank into silent meditation like an ancient Ṛishi (seer) sitting under an umbrella near the Ganges River.

After his meditation, Bhṛigu walked through the cool forest. He noticed the golden oriels spreading their bright yellow wings over the green trees. He felt the soft, warm earth under his bare feet.

"Maybe matter (*anna*) is Brahman," Bhṛigu thought. "All these beautiful things are composed of matter."

He thought,

"Out of matter these beings are born,
in matter they are sustained,
and to matter they go and merge again."

Annād dhy eva khalv imāni bhūtāni jāyante
annena jātāni jīvanti
annaṃ prayanty abhisaṃvishanti

The next day, after sweeping the kitchen, Bhṛigu asked his father, "Dear Sir, is it possible that matter is Brahman?"

"Yes, my dear son," Varuṇa answered, "matter is Brahman. And yet Brahman is more than that. Seek to know more about Brahman through meditation."

For several days Bhṛigu returned to the same spot, closed his eyes, and felt his mind become completely silent. As tamarind fruits dropped to the ground and monkeys scampered through banana trees, Bhṛigu sat peacefully in meditation by the stream.

After meditation, Bhṛigu noticed the peaceful morning breezes drifting over the water. As he breathed in, he smelled the cork tree flower, sweet like nutmeg. He thought about breath *(prāṇa)*.

"Breath must be Brahman," he reflected. "After all, no one exists without breathing. Everyone depends upon breath."

He thought,

"Out of breath these beings are born,
by breath they are sustained,
and to breath they go and merge again."

Prāṇād dhy eva khalv imāni bhūtāni jāyante
prāṇena jātāni jīvanti
prāṇaṃ prayanty abhisaṃvishanti

Bhṛigu ran back to his father, full of excitement, but out of breath! "Dear Sir," he said, "is it possible that breath is Brahman?"

"Yes, you are correct, dear son," said Varuṇa quietly.

"Breath is Brahman. And yet Brahman is more than that. Seek to know more about Brahman through meditation."

Bhṛigu knew that his father wanted him to find out the truth for himself. He knew that the knowledge he was seeking must come from within.

For several weeks Bhṛigu continued to meditate quietly every morning and evening. The silver-gray cranes dipped their long legs into the water and the snow-white egrets swooped for fish as Bhṛigu sat peacefully with closed eyes. Bhṛigu noticed that his mind was becoming more and more expanded. His mind felt playful like the forest animals, yet silent like the full moon.

One day after meditation he wondered, "Maybe mind (*manas*) is Brahman. When our minds are drowsy, we rest in the night, feeling peaceful and content. When our minds are refreshed, we awaken in the morning, feeling loving and creative."

He thought,

"Out of mind these beings are born,
in mind they are sustained,
and to mind they go and merge again."

Manaso hy eva khalv imāni bhūtāni jāyante
manasā jātāni jīvanti
manaḥ prayanty abhisaṃvishanti

That afternoon, after bringing home fruit, sugar, and nuts from the market, Bhṛigu said to his father, "Sir, I think that mind might be Brahman."

"Yes, dear son, mind is Brahman," Varuṇa answered. "And yet Brahman is more than that. Seek to know more about Brahman through meditation."

As time passed, Bhṛigu's responsibilities at home and in the village increased. He became more skillful as he milked the cow, fixed the roof, and helped his brothers and sisters with their chores.

As he continued to meditate and his mind became more and

more settled inside, Bhṛigu became aware of the orderly patterns of nature's intelligence—the cycles of the seasons and the movement of the stars. Even the orange butterfly seemed to be a picture of perfect order and intelligence.

Then Bhṛigu thought, "Intelligence (*vigyāna*) is Brahman."

He thought,

"Out of intelligence these beings are born,
through intelligence they are sustained,
and to intelligence they go and merge again."

Vigyānād dhy eva khalv imāni bhūtāni jāyante
vigyānena jātāni jīvanti
vigyānaṃ prayanty abhisaṃvishanti

Soon Bhṛigu sat next to his father. "Dear Father," he said, "could it be that intelligence is Brahman?"

Again his father answered, "My dear son, you are right. Intelligence is Brahman, and yet Brahman is more than that. Seek to know more about Brahman through meditation."

For many weeks Bhṛigu continued to meditate morning and evening. Gradually he noticed that he was enjoying his meditations more and more. A peaceful feeling blossomed in his heart. He felt clear and alert after meditation. Joy and happiness filled every moment of the day. The colored feathers of the birds, the faint rays of the sun peeking through the forest, the gurgling of the stream—all filled him with enchantment.

Bliss seemed to live in him and yet was all around him. It filled every cell of his body and every atom of the cashew nut tree, the myna bird, the water buffalo. Bliss was all that he was and bliss was all that he could see.

And then suddenly he knew that bliss (*ānanda*) is Brahman. Bliss is perfect harmony, eternal joy, perfection, and contentment.

Bhṛigu thought,

"Out of bliss these beings are born,
in bliss they are sustained,
and to bliss they go and merge again."

Ānandād dhy eva khalv imāni bhūtāni jāyante
ānandena jātāni jīvanti
ānandaṃ prayanty abhisaṃvishanti

"The whole world moves in bliss!" he thought. "Even the sun and moon stay in their orbits because of bliss."

He burst into a beautiful song: "O wonderful, O wonderful, O wonderful! I have fathomed the entire universe. I am bliss. I am Brahman (*Ahaṃ brahmāsmi*)."

As he greeted his father that evening, he didn't have to say anything. Varuṇa could see from his son's face that at last Bhṛigu knew the true nature of Brahman. Bhṛigu was radiating like the sun.

"My dear son, you have found Brahman, I see," Varuṇa said as he smiled and embraced him. "You have discovered that Brahman is bliss!"

"Yes, Father, I have found myself. I am bliss. I am Brahman. I am wholeness."

"Whoever knows the wisdom that you know, O dear Bhṛigu," said his father, "he is established in the Absolute, beyond space (*parame vyoman*).

"Whoever knows what you know in your heart, stands firm.
That person enjoys the entire creation.
That person enjoys wealth.
That person enjoys their family.
That person enjoys the love of all.
That person enjoys unbounded dignity (*mahān kīrtyā*).
That person is a knower of Brahman."

And that is how Bhṛigu discovered the wholeness of Brahman, the totality, and grew up to become a famous Ṛishi of the Veda.

आनन्दाद्ध्येव खल्विमानि भूतानि जायन्ते
आनन्देन जातानि जीवन्ति
आनन्दं प्रयन्त्यभिसंविशन्ति

Ānandād dhy eva khalv imāni bhūtāni jāyante
ānandena jātāni jīvanti
ānandaṃ prayanty abhisaṃvishanti

Out of bliss these beings are born,
In bliss they are sustained,
And to bliss they go and merge again.

Taittirīya Upanishad, 3.6.1

BĀLĀKI THE PROUD TEACHER

From the Bṛihadāraṇyaka Upanishad

The most sacred river in India is the Gangā, the River Ganges—the Granter of Wishes. Along the Ganges many holy cities can be found, but the most holy city is Vārāṇasī. In ancient times it went by the name of Kāshī. Kāshī was the most beautiful place in the world. Its lakes and gardens surpassed even the heavens in beauty. The whole city was said to float in the sky, between heaven and earth.

Early one morning, in the misty darkness before dawn, a Brahmin named Bālāki walked quietly through the narrow lanes of Kāshī in his orange robes. He was called Proud Bālāki because he took great pride in his ability to give speeches in a grand and lofty manner. He was well traveled, and was known far and wide for his exalted, silver-tongued oratory.

Just as Bālāki was a famous Sanskrit pandit, a scholar, Kāshī was a famous center of Sanskrit learning. The entire population devoted themselves to knowledge. Sanskrit pandits recited the Vedas and performed yagyas to bring balance in nature. Jyotish pandits made predictions for the future. Actors staged magical plays of the great epics, the Rāmāyaṇa and Mahābhārata. Kāshī was called the City of Light because it was self-illuminated—lit from within. It was a city devoted to the light of knowledge.

As Bālāki walked through the city, he passed many shrines and temples. The most famous was the Vishvanātha Temple to Lord Shiva, its pointed roof made of solid gold. Countless pilgrims traveled on foot to Kāshī to worship there and bathe at dawn in the Ganges, the River of Life.

By the time Bālāki reached the Ganges, it was no longer dark and he was no longer alone. As the pale sun rose, Bālāki was joined by a flood of pilgrims coming to the river for their morning bath. Everyone walked down long flights of stone steps, called *ghāts*, to the river. There Bālāki boarded a small boat and crossed the river, alone with the morning sun reflecting on the water.

On the opposite shore, Bālāki reached the glorious palace of King Ajātashatru, the Rājā of Kāshī. This king, he knew, had no enemies. Bālāki entered the court. Surrounded by ministers and attendants, the humble King Ajātashatru greeted Bālāki with hands folded in respect, for that was the customary way for a king to honor a teacher. Bālāki walked proudly up to the king.

"Your Royal Majesty," he announced in a booming voice for all the court to hear, "I would like to teach you about Brahman, wholeness of life."

"Thank you, kind Sir," the soft-spoken King Ajātashatru replied. "I would be delighted to receive your teaching. I will give you a thousand cows. Let us begin the instruction."

"Yes, Your Majesty," Bālāki said. "I will tell you about Brahman, the totality. We will begin this very moment. I understand Brahman as the sun, *Āditya*. This is the highest reality."

"Kind Sir," the intelligent king responded in a surprised tone, "I know that the sun gives radiance to all beings, creating a sparkle in their eyes. If I became the sun, then I too would give radiance to all beings. Certainly this is very good. But it is not the highest reality, which is Brahman."

Undaunted, Bālāki said, "You are right, Your Lordship. I understand that the moon, *Soma*, is Brahman."

At this King Ajātashatru was even more surprised. But still he replied modestly, "I know that the moon is the white-robed Soma, which stimulates the mind and is the essence of food. Certainly this is very good. But it is not the highest reality, which is Brahman."

Bālāki thought for a moment, and then said with authority, "I understand that lightning is Brahman."

To this the wise Ajātashatru replied, "I know that lightning is brilliance, which is found in the brightness of the skin. Certainly this is very good. But it is not the highest reality, which is Brahman."

Proud Bālāki again thought for a moment and said, "I understand that space, *ākāsha*, is Brahman."

To this King Ajātashatru replied patiently, "I know that space is full and without motion. It is found in the center of the heart, the source of love. Certainly this is very good. But it is not the highest reality, which is Brahman."

"I understand that air, *Vāyu*, is Brahman," said Bālāki, not to be silenced.

To this King Ajātashatru replied, "I know that air is found in the vital breath, and that it conquers all—when one's breath is settled, one has no enemies. Certainly this is very good. But it is not the highest reality, which is Brahman."

"I understand that fire, *Agni*, is Brahman," said Bālāki.

King Ajātashatru replied, "I know that fire is tolerant. It is found in a warm and sweet voice. Certainly this is very good. But it is not the highest reality, which is Brahman."

"I understand that water, *āpas*, is Brahman," said Bālāki.

"I know that water is harmonious and creates an agreeable nature," King Ajātashatru replied. "Certainly this is very good. But it is not the highest reality, which is Brahman."

At this point, proud Bālāki fell silent.

"Is that all?" King Ajātashatru asked respectfully.

"That is all," said Bālāki. For the first time in his life, he had nothing more to say.

"Kind Sir," the king said gently, "everything that you have told me is true. Brahman is all these things. But each one is only a part of Brahman. None alone is the totality. I do not think this teaching is enough to know Brahman."

Bālāki suddenly saw the king's wisdom. "Your Majesty," he said humbly, "will you take me as your student? I think I can learn what Brahman is from you. Please grant me this wish!"

This odd question surprised everyone in the court. "Bālāki came here as a teacher and now he wants to be a student!" they murmured to each other.

At that time in India, the various functions in life were clearly defined. Four roles were said to come from the universal Being, called *Purusha*, the administrator of the entire universe. From his head came the *Brahmins*, the teachers and scholars. From his arms came the *Kshatriyas*, the warriors and kings. From his thighs came the *Vaishyas*, the merchants and farmers. From his feet came the *Shūdras*, the laborers and sweepers.

"It is very unusual for a Brahmin like Bālāki to ask a Kshatriya like me to teach him," said King Ajātashatru. However, the compassionate king saw that Bālāki had lost his pride. And so the king said, "Yes, I will teach you what Brahman is. Come with me."

Then the king rose, took Bālāki by the hand, and led him into the royal chambers. There they came upon a member of the royal household who was sleeping.

"Let us see if we can wake him up," the king whispered to Bālāki. The king raised his voice, "O Great One, get up!"

The man slept peacefully on.

"O Radiant One, cease your slumbers!" the king cried still louder.

Still no movement.

"O Soma, awaken!" Bālāki and the king shouted together.

Nothing.

Finally, the king gently rubbed the man's hand, and he woke up.

"Where did this person go as he slept?" the king questioned Bālāki. "From what place did he return?"

"I do not know, Your Majesty," said Bālāki.

"When asleep, this man had withdrawn his senses," said the king. "His speech was withdrawn, his seeing was withdrawn, his hearing was withdrawn, and even his mind was withdrawn. While his intelligence sleeps, he resides in the space within the heart."

"What happens when he is dreaming?" Bālāki asked.

"It is as if he becomes what he dreams," said King Ajātashatru. "Whether a great king or a worthy teacher, he dreams according to his past actions. The intelligence which sleeps, the intelligence which dreams—that intelligence is Brahman."

Then the king said, "Come Bālāki. Let us enjoy the pure river Ganges." Together they boarded the large royal boat and sat in soft red chairs. As they floated by Kāshī's famous ghāts, they saw people taking their baths, cleaning their clothes, and making offerings to the river with cupped hands.

"Would you like to bathe at the royal ghāt?" the gracious king asked Bālāki.

"I would be honored," said Bālāki.

The boatmen rowed to the royal bathing ghāt. Bālāki and the king walked up the steps.

"Look, Bālāki," the king said. "Do you see that spider?"

"Yes," said Bālāki, "I see the spider moving along its web."

"We are like the spider," said the king. "We weave our life, and then move along in it. We are like the dreamer who dreams and then lives in the dream.

"This is true for the entire universe. That is why it is said, 'Having created the creation, the Creator entered into it' (*Tat shṛishtvā tad evānuprāvishat*).

"This is true for us. We create our world, and then enter into that world. We live in the world that we have created. When our hearts are pure, then we create the beautiful, enlightened life we have wished for."

As they talked, Bālāki and the king watched the pandits build a fire for the mid-day yagya. "Do you see the fire?" the king asked.

"Yes, I see the fire."

"Do you see the sparks scattering from its center?" asked the king.

"Yes, Your Majesty, I see the sparks," said Bālāki.

"The world is like the sparks," said the king. "The world is a part of Brahman just as sparks are a part of the fire.

"The sun, moon, and lightning are a part of Brahman, like the sparks in a fire.

"Our sleep, our dreams, and our whole life are a part of Brahman, like the sparks in a fire.

"Brahman is the totality. It is wholeness. And Brahman is known by knowing the Self. This is the truth of truths."

Then Bālāki realized how simple the understanding of Brahman was. He was Brahman! Brahman was himself. By knowing himself, he could know everything and do anything.

Bālāki humbly thanked the good king for giving him the supreme knowledge of Brahman—there by the Ganges, the River of Life, the Granter of Wishes.

अहं ब्रह्मास्मि

Ahaṃ brahmāsmi

I am Totality.

Bṛihadāraṇyaka Upanishad, 1.4.10

THE ASHVAMEDHA—CELEBRATION OF THE HORSE

From the Bṛihadāraṇyaka Upanishad

Cool and fresh, a gentle breeze whispered in Gopāla's ear and woke him up. For as long as he could remember, Gopāla had been waiting for this day—the day of the *Ashvamedha*, the great Celebration of the Horse. Gopāla could already hear the bells and conches calling from the festival tents, where long tables were filled with fresh fruits and cool drinks.

Gopāla's entire village spent many months preparing for this yagya, which would bring good fortune and invincibility to their Rājā, the king. Indeed, the whole kingdom would flourish and prosper from the yagya. Gopāla remembered his father's words, "Yagya is the foundation of everything. Through yagya enemies become friends."

Gopāla hopped out of bed, ran to the doorway of his family's small hut, and leaned out, swinging on the door. He saw yellow marigold blossoms lining the road, and gold banners flapping in the wind. He saw travelers from distant villages as they flowed by in a river of color. Groups of graceful women passed, the ends of their gold, red, and orange *sārīs* floating behind them like flags. Men carried woolen shawls and baskets filled with sweets. Children ducked under their parents' legs or rode in carts piled high with soft straw.

Gopāla was proud that the king chose his village for the great Ashvamedha yagya. Yesterday his family had cleaned their house, inside and out. After Gopāla and his sister swept the front step, his mother carefully chalked circles and triangles to form a colorful *mandala* (circular design). Gopāla scrubbed the cow and painted her sharp, curving horns blue. His sister hung a red rose blossom between the cow's horns.

"Gopāla!" called his mother. She finished combing his sister's long black hair, and twined it with the white blossoms of the moonbeam plant. Drifts of sweet-smelling incense tickled Gopāla's nose. He could smell the *gulāb jāmuns* (festive pastries) his grandmother was frying in a great black pot. She was singing a *bhajan*, a devotional song, in soft rhythms like the comforting swish, swish of butter churning.

"It's time to bathe in the river with your father," said his mother. "He is waiting for you in the yard."

"Yes, Mother," said Gopāla. He ran outside quickly. Today was one day he did not want to be late.

Barefooted, Gopāla followed his father on the narrow path toward the river, past groves of orange, sandalwood, and cashew-nut trees. They passed fields of pineapple, sugarcane, and rice.

Today Gopāla did not stop to look at the baby myna birds in their nest. He did not inch his way up the tall palm tree to knock down a tender, green coconut. Today he did not even wait for the bold monkeys who liked to reach inside his pockets for sweets.

Today he could not keep his father waiting. Because today his father would perform the great Celebration of the Horse with the other honored pandits of the village.

For many months Gopāla had watched his father direct the building of the *yagya-shālā*, the golden pavilion where the ceremony would be held. He watched the carpenters build the pillars—made of cedar, sandalwood, and the trees of paradise. He watched the craftsmen build beautiful gold and silver cups, used for pouring soma herbs into the fire. Gopāla's favorite part was the brick altar, shaped like a flying falcon with golden wings.

All during the past year, while the pandits chanted in the yagya-shālā, a great white horse, the finest horse in all the kingdom, had roamed the countryside. Gopāla loved to hear about the swift white stallion. Decorated with the seal of the king on its forehead, with garlands of roses looping its neck and silver bracelets circling its ankles, the horse wandered at will, claiming new land for the king.

Now the year of wandering had come to an end, and today the horse would be led through the village streets to the yagyashālā. The Celebration of the Horse would go on for three days. The pandits would perform the Ashvamedha yagya while the white horse waited nearby. After the three days of celebration, the horse would be set free.

When Gopāla and his father reached the river, they saw gray cranes with long red legs wading in the water. Women filled shiny brass pots with water, and balanced them on their heads. But missing was the ever-present chatter of the *dhobī wallahs*, the laundry men who pounded wet clothes against the rocks and stretched them out to dry in the sun.

"The river is quiet today," said Gopāla's father. "Even the lotus flowers float more lazily on the river. Perhaps they also are planning to see the Celebration of the Horse."

Gopāla smiled at his father. But his mind was on the horse. How would the grand horse feel on the last day of the celebration, when he was set free? How wonderful to run anywhere at will, through the cool moss of dense forests, over the warm sands by the ocean, along the grassy banks of rivers. As Gopāla splashed in the silky water, he imagined that the white horse was drinking beside him.

Gopāla loved to hear his father talk about the beautiful horse. As they rested on the bank of the river after their bath, he asked his father, "Sir, please tell me about the horse."

Gopāla's father began:

"The head of the horse is the dawn.
Its eye is the sun.
Its breath is the wind.
Its mouth is the universal fire.
The body of the horse is the year.
Its back is the heavens.

Its belly is the sky.
And its hoof is the earth.

Ushā vā ashvasya medhyasya shiraḥ
ūryash chakshur
vātaḥ prāṇo
vyāttam agnir vaishvānaraḥ
saṃvatsara ātmāshvasya medhyasya
dyauḥ pṛishtham
antariksham udaram
pṛithivī pājasyam

"Its sides are the four directions.
And its ribs are their midpoints.
Its limbs are the seasons.
Its joints are the months.
Its feet are the days and nights.
Its bones are the stars.
And its flesh is the clouds.

Dishaḥ pārshve
avāntaradishaḥ parshava
ṛitavo 'ngāni
māsāsh chārdhamāsāsh cha parvāṇi
ahorātrāṇi pratishthā
nakshatrāṇy asthīni
nabho māṃsāni

"Its food is the sand.
Its veins are the rivers.
Its liver and lungs are the mountains.
Its hair is the herbs and trees.
Its front is the rising sun.
And its hind is the setting sun.
When it yawns, there is lightning.
When it shakes, there is thunder.
When it makes water, there is rain.
Its neighing is speech.

Ūvadhyaṃ sikatāḥ
sindhavo gudā
yakṛich cha klomānash cha parvatā
oshadhayash cha vanaspatayash cha lomāni
udyan pūrvārdho
nimlochan jaghanārdho
yad vijṛimbhate tad vidyotate
yad vidhūnute tat stanayati
yan mehati tad varshati
vāg evāsya vāk

"The day, rising over the eastern sea,
is the golden cup in front of the horse.
The night, rising over the western sea,
is the silver cup behind the horse.
These two vessels appear before and behind the horse.
Ahar vā ashvaṃ purastān mahimā 'nvajāyata
tasya pūrve samudre yonī

rātrir enaṃ pashchān mahimā 'nvajāyata
tasyāpare samudre yonir
etau vā ashvaṃ mahimānāv abhitaḥ saṃbabhūvatuḥ

"As a steed, it carries the shining Devas,
As a stallion, it carries the celestial Gandharvas,
As a hunter, it carries the asuras,
And as a horse, it carries man."

Hayo bhūtvā devān avahad
vājī gandharvān
arvā 'surān
ashvo manushyān

Gopāla sat quietly for a few minutes, dreaming about riding the horse. Then his father said, "Gopāla, now we must hurry home. Your mother has new clothes for you. Dress quickly so we have time to practice yoga and meditation together."

At home again, Gopāla put on his new clothes. He felt fresh and clean. He went outside. His father had spread a mat on the ground, which Gopāla shared with his sister.

His father began with a short prayer,

"From non-existence lead us to existence.
From darkness lead us to light.
From death lead us to immortality."

Asato mā sad gamaya
tamaso mā jyotir gamaya
mṛityor mā amṛitaṃ gamaya

His father faced east and folded his hands together to greet the morning sun. Gopāla and his sister stretched in the warm morning sunlight, performing the yoga postures called *āsanas*. Gopāla's favorite poses were called the thunderbolt (*vajrāsana*) and the camel (*ushtrāsana*). Gopāla then practiced *prāṇāyāma* (breathing exercises).

Finally they were ready to meditate. Gopāla closed his eyes. As Gopāla meditated, he felt more and more quiet, and more and more happy. He felt full—big and expanded. He felt as wide as the sky, as vast as the infinite universe.

He thought, "My eye is the sun. My breath is the wind. When I yawn, there is lightning. And when I shake, there is thunder." Now he was ready for this fortunate day, the Celebration of the Horse.

Just after Gopāla finished meditating, he heard trumpets and drums. His arms waving in the air, Gopāla ran to the front of the house. There, being led through the streets toward the yagya-shālā, was the splendid white stallion, the precious jewel of the king.

How noble and majestic the horse looked! On its forehead the king's golden seal flashed in the sunlight. Perched high on his father's shoulders, Gopāla saw the garlands of roses looping the horse's neck and silver bracelets circling its ankles. As the great horse passed, his eyes blazed like the sun. With the horse leading the way and with joy in his heart, Gopāla held his father's hand as they joined in the grand parade to the yagya-shālā, to begin the Ashvamedha, the Great Celebration of the Horse.

पूर्णमदः पूर्णमिदं पूर्णात्पूर्णमुदच्यते
पूर्णस्य पूर्णमादाय पूर्णमेवावशिष्यते

Pūrṇam adaḥ pūrṇam idaṃ pūrṇāt pūrṇam udachyate
pūrṇasya pūrṇam ādāya pūrṇam evāvashishyate

That is full; this is full. From fullness, fullness comes out.
Taking fullness from fullness, what remains is fullness.

Bṛihadāraṇyaka Upanishad, Shānti Pātha

SHVETĀSHVATARA TEACHES ABOUT BRAHMAN

From the Shvetāshvatara Upanishad

High in the Himālayas, the Abode of Snow, small crystals of ice sparkle in the clear and fresh air. As the ice melts, it trickles down the mountain, and becomes a small stream. The stream becomes a creek, and the creek swells into a surging river. This is the most sacred river in India, the Ganges—the Stream of Nectar.

The Ganges flows from heaven to earth through deep gorges between the towering mountains. Here the air is silent, cold, and thin. The blue sky peeks from behind white and silver mountain tops. Pine trees hide many small caves. For many centuries, sitting in these caves high in the mountains, Ṛishis (seers) have practiced their meditations in silence.

One such Ṛishi in ancient times was Shvetāshvatara. For years the sage sat among the waterfalls, far above the torrent of the Ganges. From his small cave he heard the rapping of the red-headed woodpecker, trying to disturb his meditations. He heard the hum of the cicada echoing up the canyon past ferns and fields of wildflowers.

Shvetāshvatara felt satisfaction when it rained and contentment when it snowed. With joy he saw the distant peaks turn pink with the first rays of the sun. Filled with happiness, at peace with himself, he was half on earth and half in heaven.

Through his meditations, Shvetāshvatara had come to know the Self. He had become one with all he saw—mountains, misty clouds, rainbows, birds, and flowers. He was a fully enlightened sage. And yet he thought, "I am completely happy, but there is something I must do."

Some years later, Shvetāshvatara's cave was empty, but the Ganges, the River of Life, continued to flow. On its banks, the pointed roofs of shrines and āshrams (Vedic schools) touched the sky. One such āshram rested high on the cliffs above the river, at the foot of the snow-capped Himālayas. Monkeys scampered along the lime-green branches of the *pippala* tree in the quiet courtyard. The vanilla scent of frangipani blossoms mingled with the fragrance of yellow sandalwood incense.

One day, as on every other day, Shvetāshvatara, the wise sage of the Himālayas, sat under the tree in the early afternoon with a group of students. Shvetāshvatara had left his cave to become a teacher. He was teaching his students Brahma Vidyā, the knowledge of Brahman, totality of life.

Shvetāshvatara began with an invocation,

"Let us be together.

Let us eat together.

Let us be vital together.
Let us be radiating truth,
radiating the light of life.
Never shall we denounce anyone,
never entertain negativity."

Saha nāv avatu
saha nau bhunaktu
saha vīryaṃ karavāvahai
tejasvi nāv adhītam astu
mā vidvishāvahai

"Look up!" Shvetāshvatara said. "Do you see the two large birds sitting in the tree?"

"Yes, Sir, we see them," the students said.

"Do you see how one of them eats the sweet pippala berry, while the other looks on without eating?" Shvetāshvatara asked.

"We see this," the students answered.

"You are like these two birds—one part dynamic, the other

part silent. These are the two sides of your life. One part of you is active, and another part is a silent witness," Shvetāshvatara said.

"Sir, which bird is Brahman?" one student asked.

"Brahman is both together," answered Shvetāshvatara. "That is why Brahman is called the totality. No one reaches the highest tip of the tree without knowing Brahman.

"If you know only the silent bird, then you enter into darkness. If you know only the active bird, then you enter into a still greater darkness. But when you know both together, then you 'overcome death and obtain immortality' (*Avidyayā mṛityuṃ tīrtvā vidyayā amṛitam ashnute*)."

Shvetāshvatara asked, "Do you see the swan floating on the Ganges?"

"Yes, Sir, we see," answered the students.

"In this vast wheel of Brahman, which creates all things, and in which all things rest," Shvetāshvatara continued, "the swan flutters about, thinking, 'My silent Self and the world are two different things.'

"But, in truth, they are not different. Some wise people see them as one, and those people rest in evenness. They gain eternal happiness."

"Please, Sir, tell us more about Brahman," another student asked.

Shvetāshvatara replied,

"He is one.
He is without form.
Through his own great power,
and for his own unfathomable purpose,
he creates many forms.
He creates the world,
and, at the end of time,
gathers it back into himself.
May he give us clear understanding.

Ya eko 'varṇo
bahudhā shakti-yogād

varṇān anekān nihitārtho dadhāti
vi chaiti chānte vishvam ādau sa devaḥ
sa no buddhyā shubhayā saṃyunaktu

"He is Agni, the fire.
He is Āditya, the sun.
He is Vāyu, the wind.
He is Chandramā, the moon.
He is Shukra, the pure.
He is Hiraṇyagarbha, the golden womb of creation.
He is Āpas, the water.
He is Prajāpati, the protector of life.
Tad evāgnis
tad ādityas
tad vāyus
tad u chandramāḥ
tad eva shukraṃ
tad brahma

tad āpas

tat prajāpatiḥ

"You are woman.

You are man.

You are son and daughter, too.

You are the old man walking along with a staff.

Once born, you face every direction.

Tvaṃ strī

tvaṃ pumān asi

tvaṃ kumāra uta vā kumārī

tvaṃ jīrṇo daṇḍena vanchasi

tvaṃ jāto bhavasi vishvato-mukhaḥ

"You are the dark blue butterfly.

You are the green parrot with red eyes.

You are the cloud, filled with lightning.

You are the seasons and the seas.

You are without beginning.

You are everywhere.

And all that is born, is born from you."

Nīlaḥ patango

harito lohitākshas

tadid-garbha

ṛitavaḥ samudrāḥ

anādimat tvaṃ

vibhutvena vartase

yato jātāni bhuvanāni vishvā

"Please tell us how to reach Brahman," another student asked.

"Through the practice of Yoga," Shvetāshvatara said. "Through the settled mind."

"Please, Sir, how should we practice Yoga?" the student asked.

"Sit in a clean, level place that is beautiful," Shvetāshvatara said. "Let it be free from pebbles and fire, and near the sound of water. Let it be quiet, and protected from the wind.

"As you dive within, your mind will become settled, like the driver of a chariot yoked to good horses. As your mind becomes more calm, your breath will become lighter, and your body will become still and steadfast, like a rock.

"There you will find the Self, the state of union. There you will know the auspicious Brahman, the Veda, and attain unending peace. There you will follow the path of the sun."

"Please, Sir, when we start the practice of Yoga, what can we expect?" another student asked.

"The beginning fruits of Yoga are lightness, good health, steadiness, clearness of complexion, and a pleasing voice," Shvetāshvatara said.

"Just as a mirror shines bright once it has been cleaned of dust," he continued, "so those who have seen the Self shine in mind and body. They are always and forever filled with happiness.

"It would be easier to roll up the entire sky into a small cloth than it would be to obtain true happiness without knowing the Self. Only by knowing the Self does one become immortal. There is no other path."

And this is how the wise sage, Shvetāshvatara, after realizing the Self through meditation and the grace of God, spoke about Brahman as the supreme, the pure, the undivided—far above the Ganges, and far below the Himālayas, in India, the Land of the Veda, the land of knowledge.

वेदाहमेतं पुरुषं महान्तम्
आदित्यवर्णं तमसः परस्तात्
तमेव विदित्वातिमृत्युमेति
नान्यः पन्था विद्यतेऽयनाय

Vedāham etaṃ purushaṃ mahāntam
āditya-varṇaṃ tamasaḥ parastāt
tam eva viditvātimṛityum eti
nānyaḥ panthā vidyate 'yanāya

I know the Veda, the great totality,
radiant as the sun, beyond darkness.
Those who know that become immortal.
There is no other path.

Shvetāshvatara Upanishad, 3.8

THE ĀCHĀRYA'S MESSAGE ON THE LAST DAY OF STUDY

From the Taittirīya Upanishad

White sand separated the vast blue sea from the green jungle, like a strand of pearls between blue sapphires and green emeralds. The jungle was thick with sandalwood, mahogany, cashew-nut, and teakwood trees. Coconut and palmetto palms lined the sand.

A cluster of small white cottages rimmed the edge of the jungle. These bungalows served as both home and school for the teacher, the āchārya. Students lived and studied in the school, called a *guru-kula*. The cottages were surrounded by gardens of hibiscus flowers and soft grass. Peacocks and parrots played in the gardens, and monkeys scampered up and down the palms.

Every day on the grass between the cottages, the students, called *brahmachārīs*, studied with their teacher. They ate with their teacher. They sang *rāgas* (melodies) and told stories with their teacher. The students helped with the daily chores—chopping wood, carrying water, and milking the cows.

For twelve years the āchārya taught the same students. He and his wife cared for these students as their own children. The teacher clothed them and looked after their good health. He taught them how to grow food and milk the cows. Above all, the āchārya gave them knowledge.

The āchārya taught them to recite the four Vedas—Ṛik, Sāma, Yajuḥ and Atharva. He taught them correct pronunciation and meter. He gave them the many rules of Sanskrit grammar, the Veda of Vedas. He showed them how to perform the various yagyas, Vedic performances to bring good fortune and balance in nature. He instructed them in the knowledge of Jyotish, the science of prediction. He taught logic and Vedānta.

He read them the great epics, the Rāmāyaṇa and Mahābhārata, and he told them stories from the Purāṇas. He taught them mathematics, science, logic, ethics, music, art, and drama.

He taught them to exercise and play games. He showed them how to be honest and fair. He demonstrated the various postures of yoga. Most important of all, he taught them the supreme knowledge of wholeness—Brahma Vidyā.

One day in spring, as on every other day, the students gathered around the teacher in the pavilion between the bungalows. Today they chattered with excitement, because this was a special day. This was their last day in the guru-kula. After twelve years of study, the students were no longer children. They were grown up now, and would be leaving. The teacher knew that he would miss his students dearly.

The āchārya began the lesson in the usual way:

"May Mitra bring us tranquillity.
May Varuṇa bring us rest.

May Aryaman bring us quietude.
May Indra and Bṛihaspati bring us peace.
May Vishṇu of wide strides bring us contentment.

Shaṃ no mitraḥ
shaṃ varuṇaḥ
shaṃ no bhavatv aryamā
shaṃ na indro bṛihaspatiḥ
shaṃ no vishṇur uru-kramaḥ

"I give honor to Brahman.
I give honor to you, O Vāyu.
You are indeed the visible Brahman.
Indeed of you, the visible Brahman, will I speak.

Namo brahmaṇe
namas te vāyo
tvam eva pratyakshaṃ brahmāsi
tvām eva pratyakshaṃ brahma vadishyāmi

"I will speak of what is right.

I will speak of what is true.
May that satisfy me.
May that satisfy the teacher.
May I be satisfied.
May the teacher be satisfied."

Ṛitaṃ vadishyāmi
satyaṃ vadishyāmi
tan mām avatu
tad vaktāram avatu
avatu mām
avatu vaktāram

"Now, dear students, please sit," said the āchārya. He and his wife had decorated the seats with roses and orchids for this special day. The āchārya offered them milk, butter, and honey. The students recited special verses from the Vedas, and then bathed in the ocean. This ceremony, called *Samāvartana*, meant that now the students had become fully enlivened with knowledge, and were ready to return to their families.

Now it was time for the āchārya to give them a parting message:

"Speak the truth.
Do your Dharma, your natural duty.
Meditate every day.
Read the Vedas every day.
After offering to your teacher,
do not loosen the tie of affection.

"Radiate truth.
Follow Dharma, Natural Law.
Think of the welfare of others.
Enjoy prosperity.
Always continue your studies,
and be filled with devotion to God.

"Honor your mother as God.

Honor your father as God.
Honor your teacher as God.
Honor your guest as God.

Māt̤ri Devo bhava
pit̤ri Devo bhava
āchārya Devo bhava
athiti Devo bhava

"Be pure in thought and action.
Do actions you know to be good.
Be kind to those who are older.
Give to others with faith.
Do not give without faith.
Give generously.
Give modestly.
Give with sympathy.

"If you doubt an action, do as the enlightened do.
Judge your actions by those of virtuous people.

"If someone has spoken against you,
behave with kindness and love.
"Live your life in bliss.
When you are full of bliss,
you will know what is right to do.
You will know your Dharma.

"This is the knowledge.
This is the teaching.
This is the secret of the Veda.
This is the instruction.
"I have spoken what is right.
I have spoken what is true.
That has satisfied me.
That has satisfied the teacher.
I am satisfied.
The teacher is satisfied."

Ṛitam avādisham
satyam avādisham
tan mām āvīt
tad vaktāram āvīt
āvīn mām
āvīd vaktāram

Then the students presented gifts to their beloved teacher. They touched his feet and gave him woolen shawls, sweets, and garlands of orchids. They recited poems and sang songs.

"Dear Sir," one student said, "you are established in Brahman (wholeness) and learned in the Vedic scriptures. Thank you for teaching us with sweet speech and with conviction."

Another student said, "We are like the blindfolded who could not find their way home without someone to remove the blindfolds. Thank you for removing our ignorance."

"We could not have learned without our beloved teacher," said still another student. "For even someone as intelligent and well-read as King Janaka needed a teacher like you."

"We owe you a great debt for all the wisdom you have given us," said another student. "How can we ever repay you?"

The āchārya smiled fondly and replied, "You can repay me by having students of your own, and teaching them wisdom."

After much celebration, the teacher and his wife said good-bye to their students. When everyone was gone, and all was quiet, the teacher walked alone by the sea. He thought about his dear students and about how many happy moments they had spent together over the past twelve years.

In his mind's eye, he could see each student's face. He could see their faith and trust in him. He could see each of them repeating after him like frogs croaking in the rainy season—*saha nāv avatu, saha nau bhunaktu*.... He could see the students touching his feet, and offering their thanks for the knowledge they had received.

Just as students seek a good teacher, he knew that teachers also are happiest when they have ideal students. These students had not only promptly followed his wishes, but often anticipated them.

He thought of how proud he was of his students. How untroubled their minds were. How peaceful and tranquil they were. How they delighted in the Self.

He had often prayed for such students,

"May students come to me to learn the Veda.
May students come to me from all directions.
May students come to me with sincerity.
May students who are self-controlled come to me.
May students who are peaceful come to me.
May they be my wealth.
May they be my fame.

Ā māyantu brahmchāriṇaḥ svāhā
vi māyantu brahmchāriṇaḥ svāhā
pra māyantu brahmchāriṇaḥ svāhā
da māyantu brahmchāriṇaḥ svāhā

sha māyantu brahmchāriṇaḥ svāhā
yasho jane 'sāni svāhā
shreyān vasyaso 'sāni svāhā

"As water flows downwards,
as the months flow into the year,
may students come to me from all directions."
Yathāpaḥ pravatā yanti
yathā māsā aharjaram
evaṃ māṃ brahmachāriṇaḥ
dhātarāyantu sarvatas svāhā

He wandered for some time by the edge of the blue sea, lost in thought. And then suddenly he remembered, "Oh! I forgot!"

He turned and quickly hurried back to the school. There was much to be done. A new group of young students would arrive—tomorrow!

सह नाववतु
सह नौ भुनक्तु
सह वीर्यं करवावहै
तेजस्वि नावधीतमस्तु
मा विद्विषावहै

Saha nāv avatu
saha nau bhunaktu
saha vīryaṃ karavāvahai
tejasvi nāv adhītam astu
mā vidvishāvahai

Let us be together.
Let us eat together.
Let us be vital together.
Let us be radiating truth,
radiating the light of life.
Never shall we denounce anyone,
never entertain negativity.

Taittirīya Upanishad, Shānti Pātha

श्री
संहार
भैरवाय नमः

GLOSSARY OF SANSKRIT WORDS—PRONUNCIATION AND MEANING

āchārya (ah char´ yuh) teacher

Āditya (ah di´ tyuh) the sun

Agni (ug´ nee) fire

Agni Jātavedas (ug´ nee jah´ tuh vay´ dus) fire, one of the powers of nature

Ajātashatru (uh jah´ tuh shuh´ troo) the famous king of Kāshī whose name means "whose enemies (*shatru*) are unborn (*ajāta*)."

ākāsha (ah kah´ shuh) space

amṛitam (um´ ri tum) nectar of immortality

ānanda (ah´ nun duh) bliss

anna (uhn´ nuh) matter, food

āpas (ah´ pus) water

Ārtabhāga (ar´ tuh bhah´ guh) one of the pandits in the debate of King Janaka

Aryaman (ar´ yuh mun) the sun, one of the powers of nature

āsana (ah´ suh nuh) yoga posture

āshram (ahsh´ rum) Vedic school (*āshrama* in Sanskrit)

Ashvala (ush´ vuh luh) King Janaka's pandit

Ashvamedha (ush´ vuh may´ dhuh) a particular yagya, a peformance to bring balance in nature

asura (uh soo´ ruh) negative power of nature

Atharva (uh thar´ vuh) one of the four Vedas

Ātmā (aht´ mah) the Self, pure consciousness, pure awareness

Bālāki (bah´ lah kee) the proud teacher

bhajan (bhuh´ jun) hymn of praise, devotional song (*bhajana* in Sanskrit)

Bhṛigu (bhri´ goo) the son of Varuṇa

Bhujyu (bhoo´ jyoo) one of the pandits in the debate of King Janaka

Brahma Vidyā (bruh´ muh vi´ dyah) knowledge of the wholeness of life

brahmachārī (bruh´ muh chah´ ree) student

brahmacharya (bruh´ muh char´ yuh) student life

Brahman (bruh´ mun) wholeness, totality

Brahmin (brah´ min) teacher and scholar (*brāhmaṇa* in Sanskrit)

Bṛihadāraṇyaka (bri´ hud ah´ run yuh kuh) one of the ten principal Upanishads

Bṛihaspati (bri hus´ puh tee) one of the powers of nature

Chandramā (chun´ druh mah) the moon

Chhāndogya (chan do´ gyuh) one of the ten principal Upanishads

Deva (day´ vuh) positive power of nature

Dhanvantari (dhun vun´ tuh ree) "moving in a curve," the first physician

Dharma (dhar´ muh) Natural Law, natural duty

Gandharva (gun dhar´ vuh) a celestial singer

Ganesh (guh nesh´) the force of nature who removes obstacles and brings good fortune (*Ganesha* in Sanskrit)

Gangā (gun´ gah) the Ganges River (known by many names,

such as the Granter of Wishes, the River of Life, and the Stream of Nectar)

Gārgī (gar´ gee) the famous woman teacher in the debate of King Janaka

gārhasthya (gar hus´ thyuh) householder life

Gautama (gow´ tuh muh) the teacher of Satyakāma

ghāt (ghat) area with stone steps leading down into a river

Gopāla (go pah´ luh) the young boy whose father was a pandit in the Ashvamedha

guru-kula (goo´ roo koo´ luh) home and school of the teacher

Himālaya (hi mah´ luh yuh) "abode (*alaya*) of snow (*hima*)," the great snow-capped mountain range of northern India

Hiraṇyagarbha (hi run´ yuh gar´ bhuh) the golden (*hiraṇya*) womb (*garbha*) of creation

Indra (in´ druh) the leader of the Devas

Jabālā (juh bah´ lah) the mother of Satyakāma

Janaka (juh´ nuh kuh) the famous king of Videha

Jānashruti (jah´ nuh shroo´ tee) the king whose name means "celebrated (*shruti*) among the people (*jana*)."

Jyotish (jyo´ tish) the Vedic science of prediction (*Jyotisha* in Sanskrit)

kalash (kuh´ lush) the golden vessel containing amṛitam (*kalasha* in Sanskrit)

Kāshī (kah´ shee) the sacred city on the Ganges. Kāshī is the ancient name of Vārāṇasī, also called Banāras in modern times

Katha (kuh´ thuh) one of the ten principal Upanishads

Kena (kay´ nuh) "by whom," one of the ten principal Upanishads

Kshatriya (kshuh´ tree yuh) warrior or administrator

Kshiprā (kshi´ prah) one of the rivers in central India

Kumbha Melā (koom´ bhuh may´ lah) the large festival held every twelve years in Allahabad

Maghavan (muh´ ghuh vun) "Bountiful," a name for Indra

Mahābhārata (muh hah´ bhah´ ruh tuh) "Great India," one of the two great epics of India

Mahārāja (muh hah rah´ juh) great king

Maitreyī (mai tray´ ee) the beloved wife of Yāgyavalkya

manas (muh´ nus) mind

mandala (mun´ duh luh) circle (*maṇḍala* in Sanskrit)

Mitra (mi´ truh) "friendship," one of the powers of nature

Nachiketa (nuh chi kay´ tuh) the son of Vājashravas (sometimes written Nachiketas)

namaste (nuh´ mus tay´) Greetings! I bow down to you.

pandit (pun´ dit) learned scholar, one who performs yagyas and chants the Vedas (*paṇḍita* in Sanskrit)

Prajāpati (pruh jah´ puh tee) "lord of creation," the protector of life, one of the powers of nature

prāṇa (prah´ nuh) breath, vital force

prāṇāyāma (prah´ nah yah´ muh) breathing exercise

Purāṇa (poo rah´ nuh) "ancient." There are eighteen Purāṇas in the Vedic Literature.

Purusha (poo´ roo shuh) universal Being, the unbounded Self

rāga (rah´ guh) melody, song

Raikva (rai´ kvuh) the enlightened cart driver

rājā (rah´ jah) king

Rāmāyaṇa (rah´ mah´ yuh nuh) "the story of Rāma," one of the two great epics of India

Ṛik (rik) the first of the four Vedas

Ṛishi (ri´ shee) seer, sage

Sāma (sah´ muh) one of the four Vedas

Sāmashravas (sah´ muh shruh´ vus) the young pupil and servant of Yāgyavalkya

Samāvartana (suh mah´ var´ tuh nuh) the bathing ceremony at the end of one's studies

sannyāsa (sun nyah´ suh) retired life

Satyakāma (suh´ tyuh kah´ muh) the young boy whose name means "seeker (*kāma*) of truth (*satya*)"

Shiva (shee´ vuh) the power of nature responsible for evolution

Shūdra (shoo´ druh) laborer or sweeper

Shukra (shoo´ kruh) "the pure," the planet Venus

Shvetaketu (shvay´ tuh kay´ too) the son of Uddālaka

Shvetāshvatara (shvay tash´ vuh tuh ruh) the Ṛishi who becomes a teacher, the name of the Upanishad in which he is the teacher

Sītā (see´ tah) the daughter of King Janaka

Soma (so´ muh) the moon, the juice used in performing a yagya

svāhā (svah´ hah´) Hail! (said while making offerings to the yagya fire)

Taittirīya (tait´ ti ree´ yuh) one of the ten principal Upanishads

tapas (tuh´ pus) "inner glow," meditation

Uddālaka (ood dah´ luh kuh) Shvetaketu's father

Umā (oo´ mah) the daughter of the Himālayas

Upanayana (oo´ puh nuh´ yuh nuh) the initiation ceremony, qualifying a person to study the Vedic Literature and practice meditation

Upanishad (oo puh´ ni shud) "to sit down near," an aspect of Vedic Literature concerned with the nature of pure consciousness

ushtrāsana (oosh trah´ suh nuh) the yoga āsana pose of the camel

vajrāsana (vuh jrah´ suh nuh) the yoga āsana pose of the thunderbolt

Vaishya (vai´ shyuh) merchant or farmer

Vājashravas (vah´ jush ruh´ vus) the father of Nachiketa

vānaprasthya (vah´ nuh prus´ thyuh) forest dweller life

Vārāṇasī (vah´ rah nuh see) the modern name of Kāshī

Varuṇa (vuh´ roo nuh) the father of Bhṛigu; also water, one of the powers of nature

Vāyu (vah´ yoo) wind or air, one of the powers of nature

Vāyu Mātarishvan (vah´ yoo mah´ tuh rish´ vun) wind or air, one of the powers of nature

Veda (vay´ duh) pure knowledge, the fundamental structures of Natural Law at the basis of the universe. "The Vedas" usually refers to the four Vedas: Ṛik, Sāma, Yajuḥ, and Atharva. "Vedas" can also refer to the Vedic Literature as a whole.

Vedānta (vay dan´ tuh) "culmination of the Veda," an aspect of the Vedic Literature

Videha (vi day´ huh) the kingdom in ancient India ruled by

King Janaka

vigyāna (vi gyah´ nuh) intelligence

Virochana (vi ro´ chuh nuh) one of the asuras

Vishṇu (vish´ noo) the force of nature that maintains creation

Vishvanātha (vish´ vuh nah´ thuh) the most famous temple in Vārāṇasī

yagya (yuh´ gyuh) performance that creates balance in nature

yagya-shālā (yuh´ gyuh shah´ lah) the hall constructed for the yagya

Yāgyavalkya (yah´ gyuh vul´ kyuh) the famous teacher who wins the debate of King Janaka

Yajuḥ (yuh´ jooh) one of the four Vedas

Yama (yuh´ muh) the administrator of death and immortality

Yoga (yo´ guh) union, the settled mind; also, the various practices for settling the mind, such as yoga āsanas and meditation

yogī (yo´ gee) one who has attained yoga

ABOUT THE AUTHORS

Kumuda Reddy, M.D.

Kumuda Reddy, M.D., has practiced medicine for twenty years. She completed her residency and fellowship in anesthesiology at Mt. Sinai Hospital, New York.

Dr. Reddy is a former faculty member and anesthesiologist at Albany Medical College. She is currently an adjunct faculty member there, and directs the Maharishi Ayur-Veda Health Center of Upstate New York. In addition to writing and lecturing extensively on the Maharishi Vedic Approach to Health, Dr. Reddy writes books based on the traditional stories of India.

Dr. Reddy lives in Niskayuna, New York, with her husband Janardhan, a practicing urologist, and her three children, Sundeep, Suma, and Hima.

Thomas Egenes, Ph.D.

Thomas Egenes has published the textbook *Introduction to Sanskrit*, which has been translated into Dutch and German, as well as a workbook, flashcards, audiotapes, and videotapes for the study of Sanskrit. Dr. Egenes has given presentations on Sanskrit in India, Europe, Canada, and throughout the United States. He is an Associate Professor at Maharishi University of Management in Fairfield, Iowa, where he has taught Sanskrit to more than 3,000 students during the past fifteen years.

Dr. Egenes received his B.A. from the University of Notre Dame and his M.A. and Ph.D. from the University of Virginia.

Linda Egenes, M.A.

Linda Egenes writes books for both adults and children. A life-long educator, she currently teaches literary journalism at Maharishi University of Management in Fairfield, Iowa. Ms. Egenes has a B.S. in elementary education from Illinois State University and an M.A. in professional writing from Maharishi University of Management.

New Natural Health Titles from Samhita Productions

For a Blissful Baby
Healthy and Happy Pregnancy with
Maharishi Vedic Medicine
by Kumuda Reddy, M.D., Linda Egenes, M.A.,
Margaret Mullins, R.N.

Conquering Chronic Disease
Through Maharishi Vedic Medicine
by Kumuda Reddy, M.D.

Forever Healthy
Introduction to Maharishi Ayur-Veda Health Care
by Kumuda Reddy, M.D. & Stan Kendz

New Inspirational Titles from Samhita Productions

The Eternal Story of Love
by Kumuda Reddy

East, West and Sideways
by Kumuda Reddy & Mary Leete

The Timeless Wisdom Series of Children's Stories

The Indigo Jackal
The Lion and the Hare
The Monkey and the Crocodile
The Female Mouse
The Priceless Bird
The Hares and the Elephants
The Hawks and Their Friends
The Miser's Reform
Prince Fearless
The Small Birds and the Great Ocean
The True Treasure
The Three Fishes
The Three Thieves
The Dog King
The Washerman's Donkey
The King's Minister
Prince Peaceful
The King's New Shoes
The Fragrant Deer
Madhu the Antelope
The Royal Elephant
The Old Snake and the Frogs
The Stolen Jewels
The Turtle and the Swans
The Lions and the Baby Jackal
The Wish That Came True

For more information please contact:

Samhita Productions
1537 Union Street
Schenectady, New York 12309
Visit us on the web at: www.allhealthyfamily.com
Phone: 1-888-603-9171
Fax: 1-518-393-6301
or e-mail us at: information@allhealthyfamily.com